More
REEF FISHES
& NUDIBRANCHS

EAST AND SOUTH COAST OF SOUTHERN AFRICA

More
REEF FISHES
& NUDIBRANCHS

EAST AND SOUTH COAST OF SOUTHERN AFRICA

DENNIS KING
& VALDA FRASER

ACKNOWLEDGEMENTS

Firstly I must express my appreciation to Valda Fraser, my co-author, for responding with such enthusiasm to my suggestion that she write the Nudibranch section of this book. In the relatively short time of her involvement with nudibranchs and underwater photography, she has become most knowledgeable on the identification of nudibranchs and an accomplished photographer.

Our sincere thanks to Mike Fraser, Valda's husband, for all the hours spent diving together. His skills in sea-manship and navigation and his enthusiasm for the sport are remarkable. I would like to thank Neville and Wendy Ayliffe of Reefteach (dive charters), Sodwana Bay, for their hospitality and for Neville's local fish and reef knowledge, which he willingly shared with me. Also Roux le Noury and his staff of Dive Nautique, Umhlanga, for their assistance with dives.

The following authorities need to be thanked for giving their time and expertise to confirm identifications and to comment on the text: Dr Phil Heemstra and Elaine Heemstra (fish), Simon Chater (fish), Bruce and Judy Mann (fish/text), Dr Anthony Gill (Dotty backs), Rudie Kuiter (Pipefish), Guido Zsilavecz (Klip fish), Dr Helen Larson (Gobies), Nerida Wilson (nudibranchs), and Bill Rudman (nudibranchs). A special word of thanks is due to Nat Kistnasamy for updating and drawing new fish and nudibranch illustrations.

My gratitude also goes to the Seaworld Aquarium, Durban and the Two Oceans Aquarium, Cape Town for the opportunity of taking fish photographs inside the main tanks.

To my wife, Irma, a very special thanks for her support and encouragement and the hours she has spent typing many drafts of the text. Valda would also like to thank her family for their support and understanding.

Finally we would both like to express our appreciation and thanks to Pippa Parker (Publishing Manager), Helen de Villiers (Managing Editor), Katharina von Gerhardt (Editor), Bridgitte Chemaly (Designer), and the rest of the Struik team involved, for doing such excellent work in putting this book together.

PHOTOGRAPHIC NOTES

The fish photographs were taken with a Nikon F single lens reflex camera in an Ikelite housing together with an Ikelite Substrobe 200. Lenses used included a 55 mm macro, 105 mm macro and 28 mm. For the larger fish and underwater scenes a Nikonos V camera with a 15 mm lens was used.

The nudibranchs photographs were generally taken with a Nikonos V camera with either a 1:1 or 2:1 extension tube and an Ikelite Substrobe 100. The above mentioned housed camera with a 105 mm macro lens was also used. Fujichrome Provia 100 ASA film was used almost exclusively.

PHOTOGRAPHIC CREDITS

Fish Section – all photographs by Dennis King except for:
- Jenny Smart – Front cover – centre fish • Jeremy Cliff – page 17.4, 19.2 and 63.4 • Dale Southern – page 99.4 • Alan Mountain – page 93.5

Nudibranchs Section – all photographs by Valda Fraser except for :
- Dennis King – page 115.4, 117.3, 119.2, 121.4, 121.5, 125.2 and 129.4 • Ian Miller – page 112 bottom left
- Jenny-Lynne Gray – page 129.2

Struik Publishers
(a division of New Holland Publishing
(South Africa) (Pty) Ltd)
80 McKenzie Street
Cape Town 8001
South Africa

Visit us at **www.struik.co.za**
Log on to our photographic website **www.imagesofafrica.co.za**
for an African experience

New Holland Publishing is a member of the Johnnic
Publishing Group
First edition published in 2002

10 9 8 7 6 5 4 3 2

Copyright © in published edition: Struik Publishers 2001
Editor: Katharina von Gerhardt
Designer: Bridgitte Chemaly
Cover design: Robin Cox
Cartographer: James Whitelaw
Reproduction: Hirt & Carter Cape (Pty) Ltd, Cape Town
Printed by: Times Offset (M) Sdn Bhd

ISBN 1 86872 686 X

FRONT COVER (TOP TO BOTTOM): Yellowtail wrasse, Ribbon eel, Tiger rockcod. Inset: *Chromodoris geminus*. PAGE 1: Tomato rockcod. PAGE 5: Tiger angelfish. PAGE 7: Natal knifejaw. PAGE 9: Coachman. PAGE 10: Coral rockcod. PAGE 110: *Janolus capensis*. PAGE 131: Sulphur damsel. PAGE 132: *Halgerda wasinensis*.

CONTENTS

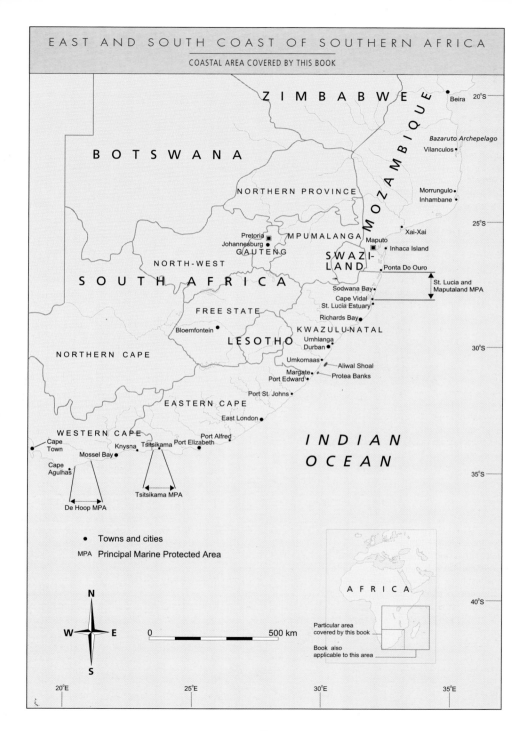

EAST AND SOUTH COAST OF SOUTHERN AFRICA

COASTAL AREA COVERED BY THIS BOOK

ZIMBABWE

Beira

20°S

BOTSWANA

MOZAMBIQUE

Bazaruto Archepelago
Vilanculos

NORTHERN PROVINCE

Morrungulo
Inhambane

25°S

Pretoria
Johannesburg
GAUTENG

MPUMALANGA

Xai-Xai

Maputo

Inhaca Island

NORTH-WEST

SWAZI-
LAND

Ponta Do Ouro

St. Lucia and
Maputaland MPA

SOUTH AFRICA

Sodwana Bay
Cape Vidal
St. Lucia Estuary

Richards Bay

FREE STATE

Bloemfontein

KWAZULU-NATAL

LESOTHO

Umhlanga
Durban

30°S

NORTHERN CAPE

Umkomaas
Margate
Port Edward

Aliwal Shoal
Protea Banks

Port St. Johns

EASTERN CAPE

East London

WESTERN CAPE

Port Alfred

Cape
Town

Knysna Tsitsikama Port Elizabeth

Mossel Bay

INDIAN

Cape
Agulhas

OCEAN

35°S

Tsitsikama MPA

De Hoop MPA

- Towns and cities
MPA Principal Marine Protected Area

AFRICA

40°S

N

W   E

0   500 km

Particular area
covered by this book

S

Book also
applicable to this area

20°E

25°E

30°E

35°E

6

THE VAST AND CONTRASTING southern African coast boasts a staggering variety of fauna and flora. This diversity may be attributed to the two major currents sweeping past the western and eastern coasts of the continent. The warm Southern Equatorial Current, which is a huge wind-driven water mass moving in an anti-clockwise direction in the Indian Ocean, splits upon reaching the northern tip of Madagascar. To the south, near the coast of KwaZulu-Natal, the two currents straddling the island of Madagascar rejoin to form the mighty Agulhas Current. This warm water brings a plethora of tropical Indo-Pacific species to the eastern shores of southern Africa. To the west, the Antarctic Circumpolar Current flows from west to east in the Southern Ocean, giving rise to the Benguela Current. This cold, nutrient-rich water flows north-wards along the west coast of southern Africa and is extremely rich in plankton, which feeds other animals higher up in the food-chain, notably sardine and anchovy.

The range of habitats, such as lagoons and estuaries, sandy beaches and rocky shores, coral reefs and the open oceans, are further in-fluenced by various physical factors such as temperature, prevailing winds, light inten-sity, and salinity. As a result, marine creatures have adapted in many different, and often wondrous ways to their particular environments.

Natal Knifejaw

Many of the species of fish that occur in the waters off the east coast of southern Africa have been dis-cussed in my previous book *Reef Fishes and Corals, East Coast of Southern Africa* (Struik, 1996). As many scuba divers, snorkellers and marine aquarists have shown such a keen interest in the book it was only natural for me to write a follow-up book. The result is *More Reef Fishes and Nudibranchs, East and South Coast of Southern Africa*. It should be viewed as a companion to the first book, for together they cover some 493 differ-ent species of marine fishes encountered by scuba divers and snorkellers. It should be noted that the butterflyfish family is represented by only two species in this book as they were extensively covered in the previous book.

In addition, an identification guide for the more com-mon species of nudibranchs or seaslugs (as they are also known) has been included. This section will intro-duce readers to some of these remarkable animals, incredibly variable in colour, shape, size and texture. They live in diverse habitats – from tidal pools along rocky shores to the coastal reefs of all seas around the world. Hopefully the information provided will help readers to identify the nudibranchs they find, and learn more about them.

This book is not intended in any way to be a scientific work. As such, details regarding the anatomy of fish, the number of fin rays, etc. are not included. Only lim-ited information on nudibranch biology and taxonomy is provided. The use of scientific terminology has been restricted. Readers who wish to pursue their interest in fishes and nudibranchs should consult the publications listed under the *References* and *Suggested Further Reading* section on page 132.

Many of the fish and nudibranch species described in this book have a wider distribution than southern Africa, and therefore visitors to East Africa, the Sey-chelles, the Comoros, Mauritius, Madagascar and the Maldives will also find this book to be extremely useful. Each species entry includes the most noteworthy descriptive features, geographical distribu-tion, habitat, depth range and diet, where known.

For each species of fish and nudibranch discussed, a clear, full-colour photograph is pro-vided in order to assist the reader with accurate identifi-cation. Descriptions of fish colours may be problematic, as certain fish are able to change colour according to their mood and surroundings. In addition, colours and shapes of juveniles can be very different from those of adults. The depth of the water further influences colour as the red end of the visible colour spectrum filters out as the depth increases. This causes the true colour to become distorted. A strobe light was used to capture the true colours. Therefore the colours shown in the photographs are not necessarily those seen underwater. A description in the text stating that colour 'varies from reddish brown to olive-brown or grey' indicates that it could be any of those colours or shades in between.

The maximum recorded size attained for each fish or nudibranch species is included, but since most indi-viduals never reach this size, the diver will generally see smaller specimens than those indicated.

The depth range of fishes and nudibranchs may well be found to be shallower or deeper than stated.

A common name is provided for each fish species, primarily based on *Smith's Sea Fishes* (Southern Book Publishers, 1988). Where relevant, alternative names are given in parentheses. The scientific name of each fish species is provided, and the species are grouped into families.

In the nudibranch section, the scientific (Latin) name has been used in discussing each species. The reason for this is twofold: in most instances, common names of nudibranchs do not exist. Secondly, it eliminates the confusion that arises should a particular species be known by a number of common names. However, where the common name is widely known and accepted, as for example with the Spanish dancer (*Hexabranchus sanguineus*), it has been included.

By studying this book for just one or two hours, readers will be amazed how quickly they will learn to recognize the creatures depicted. The ability to identify species will increase rapidly after only a few dives. The real fun begins when an unfamiliar species is sighted. You become an underwater detective, looking for clues that might reveal the identity of the 'mystery' fish or nudibranch. Alertness, stalking skills (in the case of fish), attention to detail, and a good memory make for excellent and rewarding sightings. These skills develop in time and with practice, and soon you will be able to remember sufficient detail in order to identify the animals in this book. Of course, if you have an underwater camera, the identification process becomes much easier.

Sport divers and snorkellers can play a valuable role in assisting marine biologists by recording observations of animal behaviour and new distribution records, and even possibly discovering new species. This is part of the excitement of being interested in marine fauna, where many creatures still await classification and description.

When diving, remember to abide by the rules for safe diving and to avoid touching the reef. As a diver, be aware of the importance of preserving the underwater environment and help prevent it from being spoiled by human thoughtlessness, ignorance and greed, so that future generations can also enjoy our precious, but fragile underwater world.

HOW TO USE THIS BOOK

FISH SECTION

To identify a fish species, it is first necessary to decide to which family it belongs. To assist with this process, clear line drawings of the fish families are displayed on pages 12-15. These have been grouped together based on shared characteristics, such as 'silvery in colour' or 'odd-shaped swimmers' etc. To identify a fish correctly, first decide to which group it belongs, then look for the family by studying the line drawings. A page reference refers the reader to photographs of individual species for further identification. Details of each species are given in the text opposite, together with the physical characteristics, distinguishing features, geographical distribution, habitat and habits, depth range, diet, abundance and, where relevant, species it may be confused with.

When spotting a fish, try to memorize certain features such as overall shape, colour, patterns and position of spots or lines. Other features, such as the presence of one or two dorsal fins, a round or forked tail etc. may also help. Remember that the colour of a fish can change with depth. Take the time to study the various families and get to know them, as this will greatly assist with your identifications.

ABBREVIATIONS

sp = species. Used in scientific terminology where an animal has yet to be described, or identification is not certain.

cf = compare. Refers reader to another similar species.

NUDIBRANCH SECTION

The focus of this section is to introduce and familiarize the reader with a number of fascinating marine slugs. A general introduction on nudibranchs with illustrations, depicting basic nudibranch anatomy, is given on page 112.

Detailed descriptions of each family and individual species are given in the text opposite the photographs. The species descriptions outline physical characteristics and distinguishing features in order to facilitate identification. Geographical distribution, habitat, depth range, diet (where possible) and abundance are also included.

The name of the person who described the particular nudibranch and the year of description have been noted. Brackets are used if a species has been moved to another genus due to taxonomic revision.

EXPLANATION OF SCIENTIFIC NAMES

The scientific name of animals comprises two words: the first word refers to the genus – a group of animals or plants sharing similar characteristics (e.g. *Chromodoris*). The second word indicates the species name (e.g. *hamiltoni*), often derived from a person's name e.g. the name of the person who first found the species, a friend of the author, or in honour of a particular scientist. In some instances, the name links with the place where the animal was first collected or an outstanding external characteristic feature.

FISHES

Cartilaginous fishes
Class Chondrichthyes

Cartilaginous fishes include sharks, rays, guitarfishes and sawfishes. Although they resemble bony fishes in general design and anatomy, they have a number of distinguishing characteristics. The most significant feature is the structure of the skeleton which, unlike that of bony fishes, is composed of cartilage, and not of true bone. The five to seven gill slits of cartilaginous fishes are exposed, whereas in bony fishes the delicate gill chambers are protected by a single gill cover. The jaws have rows of either well-defined teeth or fused plates (flat, pavement-like teeth). The teeth are continuously replaced throughout the life of the animal. The fins of cartilaginous fishes also differ from those of bony fishes as they are fleshy, spineless (except for the spiny dogfish) and lack fin-rays. Rays and guitarfishes have enormously enlarged pectoral fins that are fused to the head. Cartilaginous fish lack the typical scales of bony fish. Their skin is nevertheless rough and abrasive and in the case of sharks, this is due to teeth-like projections called dermal denticles.

All cartilaginous fishes are carnivorous, with bottom-dwelling sharks and rays feeding mainly on molluscs and crustaceans, while pelagic sharks prey on larger fish and marine mammals. Sharks lack a swim bladder; instead they use their enlarged oil-filled liver for buoyancy. They possess a keen sense of smell and are able to detect vibrations through sensitive nerve cells in the lateral line system, as well as detect changes in electric fields through special structures on the head. These sensory functions assist in accurate prey detection and possibly navigation.

Reproduction in chondrichthyans is complex and is characterized by internal fertilization, accomplished by the paired claspers of the male. Mating is followed by one of three developmental patterns: most cartilaginous fishes are ovoviviparous and give birth to live young; while some cartilaginous fishes (certain sharks and rays) are oviparous and lay eggs that are encapsulated by a horny case and deposited on the substrate. Yet others are viviparous and retain the developing embryos in the oviducts (uterus), receiving direct nourishment from the mother until the young are born. Live-bearing sharks and rays have a typical gestation period that lasts about 12 months, but varies between species from 6–22 months. Litter sizes vary between 1 or 2 and 136 young. Fewer than 20 young per litter is more usual.

About 370 different species of shark and over 500 species of ray have been identified worldwide.

Bony fishes
Class Osteichthyes

Bony fishes have a true bone skeleton and flexible fins supported by spines and rays. A single gill cover on either side of the head protects the gill chamber, which houses the respiratory gill arches and filaments. The majority of bony fishes are covered with a protective layer of scales, although a few families, such as barbels, blennies and eels, are scaleless. Many bony fishes have a swim bladder which they use to control buoyancy. They are able to detect vibrations and pressure changes in the water via a series of sense organs located along the lateral line. External fertilization is common in marine bony fishes, with large numbers of eggs and sperm being released into the water. Some fishes such as damselfishes lay their eggs on the substratum, where they are fertilized directly. An important feature in the reproduction of some bony fishes is the ability to change sex. The determinants of sex change may be genetic or environmental. Certain fishes are born female, but change sex to male when they attain a particular size. Other species change from male to female, while others can reverse their sex when necessary. This process helps to ensure maximum reproductive potential of the particular species.

Bony fishes display a vast array of shapes, colours, sizes, behaviour patterns and adaptations. They are found in such diverse environments as estuaries, sandy beaches, rocky shores, inshore and offshore reefs and the ocean depths, not to mention freshwater habitats.

Bony fishes form the largest group of vertebrate animals on earth. Some 22 000 species have been recorded in all aquatic habitats.

Coral rockcod

External features of fish

The external features of cartilaginous and bony fishes referred to in the identification process are indicated in the diagrams below.

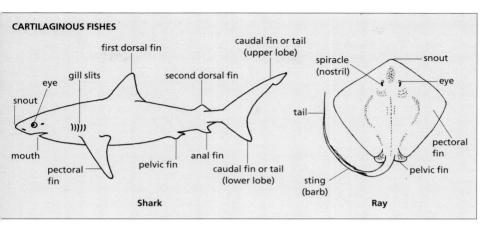

CARTILAGINOUS FISHES

Shark labels: caudal fin or tail (upper lobe), first dorsal fin, second dorsal fin, gill slits, eye, snout, mouth, pectoral fin, pelvic fin, anal fin, caudal fin or tail (lower lobe)

Ray labels: spiracle (nostril), snout, eye, tail, pectoral fin, pelvic fin, sting (barb)

Shark

Ray

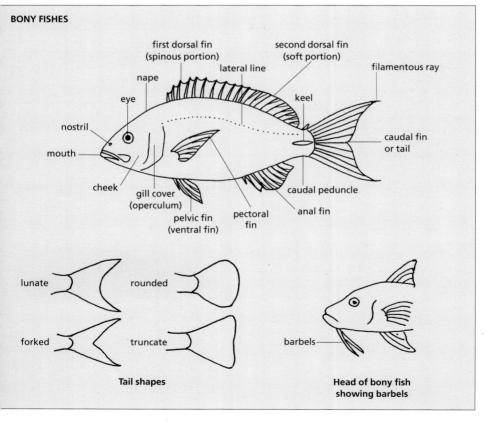

BONY FISHES

Labels: first dorsal fin (spinous portion), second dorsal fin (soft portion), lateral line, filamentous ray, nape, eye, keel, nostril, mouth, caudal fin or tail, cheek, gill cover (operculum), caudal peduncle, pelvic fin (ventral fin), pectoral fin, anal fin

Tail shapes: lunate, rounded, forked, truncate

Tail shapes

barbels

Head of bony fish showing barbels

11

Identification groups and pictorial guide to fish families

The following illustrations are line-drawings of the fish families contained in this book. Families sharing a common characteristic are grouped together for initial identification.

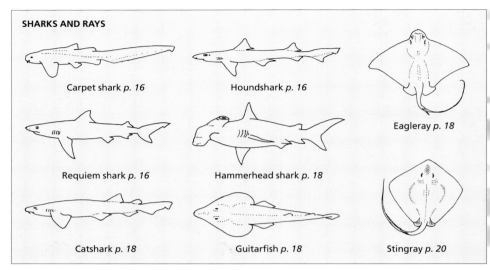

SHARKS AND RAYS

Carpet shark *p. 16*

Houndshark *p. 16*

Eagleray *p. 18*

Requiem shark *p. 16*

Hammerhead shark *p. 18*

Catshark *p. 18*

Guitarfish *p. 18*

Stingray *p. 20*

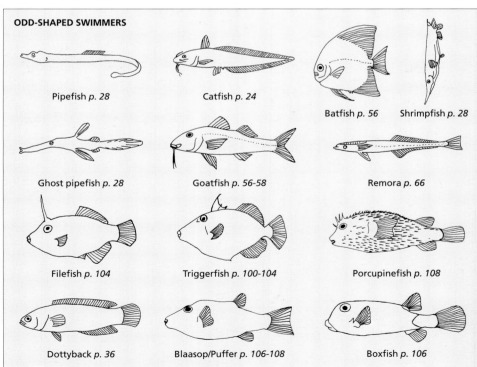

ODD-SHAPED SWIMMERS

Pipefish *p. 28*

Catfish *p. 24*

Batfish *p. 56*

Shrimpfish *p. 28*

Ghost pipefish *p. 28*

Goatfish *p. 56-58*

Remora *p. 66*

Filefish *p. 104*

Triggerfish *p. 100-104*

Porcupinefish *p. 108*

Dottyback *p. 36*

Blaasop/Puffer *p. 106-108*

Boxfish *p. 106*

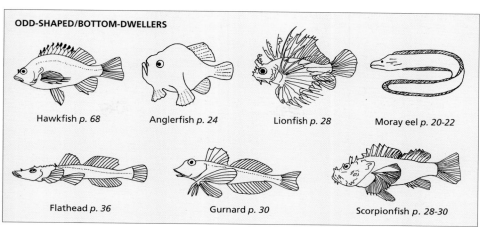

ODD-SHAPED/BOTTOM-DWELLERS

Hawkfish *p. 68*

Anglerfish *p. 24*

Lionfish *p. 28*

Moray eel *p. 20-22*

Flathead *p. 36*

Gurnard *p. 30*

Scorpionfish *p. 28-30*

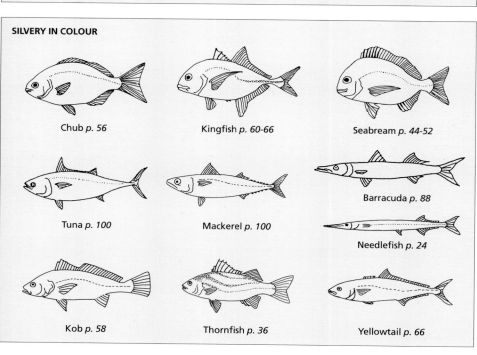

SILVERY IN COLOUR

Chub *p. 56*

Kingfish *p. 60-66*

Seabream *p. 44-52*

Tuna *p. 100*

Mackerel *p. 100*

Barracuda *p. 88*

Needlefish *p. 24*

Kob *p. 58*

Thornfish *p. 36*

Yellowtail *p. 66*

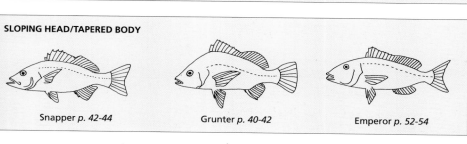

SLOPING HEAD/TAPERED BODY

Snapper *p. 42-44*

Grunter *p. 40-42*

Emperor *p. 52-54*

DISC OR OVAL-SHAPED/COLOURFUL

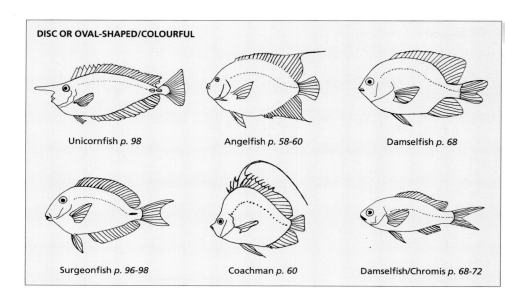

Unicornfish *p. 98*

Angelfish *p. 58-60*

Damselfish *p. 68*

Surgeonfish *p. 96-98*

Coachman *p. 60*

Damselfish/Chromis *p. 68-72*

HEAVY BODY/LARGE LIPS

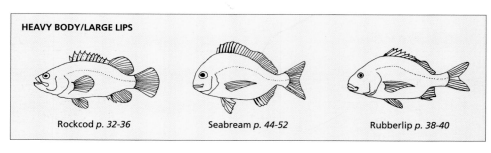

Rockcod *p. 32-36*

Seabream *p. 44-52*

Rubberlip *p. 38-40*

BIG EYES/CAVE-DWELLERS

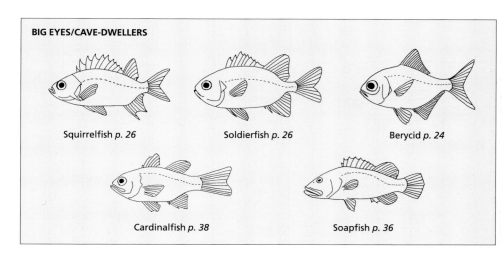

Squirrelfish *p. 26*

Soldierfish *p. 26*

Berycid *p. 24*

Cardinalfish *p. 38*

Soapfish *p. 36*

REGULAR-SHAPED SWIMMERS

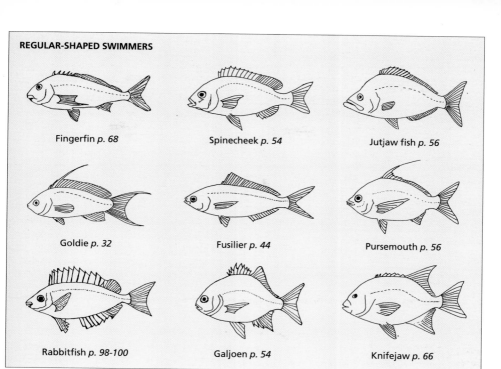

Fingerfin *p. 68*

Spinecheek *p. 54*

Jutjaw fish *p. 56*

Goldie *p. 32*

Fusilier *p. 44*

Pursemouth *p. 56*

Rabbitfish *p. 98-100*

Galjoen *p. 54*

Knifejaw *p. 66*

SWIM WITH PECTORAL FINS

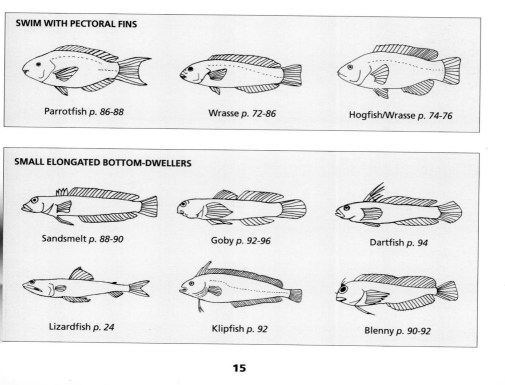

Parrotfish *p. 86-88*

Wrasse *p. 72-86*

Hogfish/Wrasse *p. 74-76*

SMALL ELONGATED BOTTOM-DWELLERS

Sandsmelt *p. 88-90*

Goby *p. 92-96*

Dartfish *p. 94*

Lizardfish *p. 24*

Klipfish *p. 92*

Blenny *p. 90-92*

SHARKS

Sharks have cartilaginous skeletons and rough skins covered with tiny teeth-like projections. Five to seven gill slits occur on either side of the head. Males have paired claspers used for mating. Sharks are solitary but may congregate during the mating season. Most are harmless, but some are potentially dangerous to man.

Carpet sharks – Family Orectolobidae

LEOPARD SHARK (ZEBRA SHARK) – *Stegostoma fasciatum*

Attains 250 cm. Elongated body with prominent dorsal ridges and an extremely long, broad tail. Adults are yellowish brown with scattered dark spots. Juveniles range in colour from dark brown to black with yellow bars along the body and tail. This solitary bottom-dweller is often found resting on the sand near reefs at depths of between 5-40 m. Feeds mainly at night on molluscs, invertebrates and small fish. Distributed throughout tropical Indo-West Pacific, extending south to KwaZulu-Natal. This uncommon shark is docile and harmless and is often accompanied by remora fish.

Whale Sharks – Family Rhincodontidae

WHALE SHARK – *Rhincodon typus*

Can attain 14 m or more. The world's largest living fish is easily recognized by its pattern of white spots and bars on upper body. Blunt, flat head with a large mouth. Blue-grey dorsally, and white ventral surface. Ranges in depth from 1-130 m. Cruises about with its mouth open, filtering large volumes of water to extract food such as plankton, small fishes and squid. Often swims just below surface whilst feeding. Found in all tropical and sub-tropical waters. Seasonally common off KwaZulu-Natal and Mozambique. An encounter with this curious, yet harmless shark is an unforgettable experience.

Requiem sharks – Family Carcharhinidae

SHORTNOSE BLACKTAIL REEF SHARK – *Carcharhinus wheeleri*

Attains 170 cm. A stout, medium-sized shark identified by a prominent black band on rear edge of tail fin, and white edging on tip of first dorsal fin. Body colour is dark grey or bronze dorsally, and white ventrally. This coastal shark is associated with coral reefs and ranges in depth from 3-140 m. Feeds on small fish, octopus and squid. Only occurs in the western Indian Ocean from northern KwaZulu-Natal to the Red Sea. Considered uncommon and may be aggressive to spearfishermen with speared fish.

WHITETIP REEF SHARK (BLUNTHEAD SHARK) – *Triaenodon obesus*

Attains 210 cm. Medium-sized slender shark with an extremely short, broad snout. Best identified by the conspicuous white tips on first dorsal fin and upper lobe of tail fin. The second dorsal fin may also have a white tip. Body colour is grey or brown dorsally, with a lighter underside. May have dark spots on sides. Found singly or in small groups and favours shallow inshore coral reefs, ranging in depth from 8-40 m. Hunts for fish, octopus and larger crustaceans in crevices in the reef at night. Widely distributed throughout tropical Indo-Pacific, extending to southern KwaZulu-Natal. A common shark that often approaches divers, but is not considered dangerous.

Houndsharks – Family Triakidae

HOUNDSHARK (SMOOTH HOUND SHARK) – *Mustelus mustelus*

Attains 160 cm. General body colour is grey-brown, sometimes with distinct black spots on upper surface. Underside is pale. Fairly large caudal fin with notched tip. Eyes are green and large. Inhabits mainly shallow sandy shores, but also occurs at depths of 350 m. Feeds on crabs, lobsters, shrimps and bony fishes. Widespread throughout eastern Atlantic Ocean and the Mediterranean Sea, and ranges locally from KwaZulu-Natal to Namibia. A fairly common yet shy shark rarely encountered by divers.

Catsharks – Family Scyliorhinidae

PUFFADDER SHYSHARK – *Haploblepharus edwardsii*

Attains 60 cm. Small, elongated shark with a short snout and a robust head. Distinctive colour pattern consists of a sandy-brown background, overlaid with seven reddish-brown, dark rimmed saddles. Numerous dark brown and white spots between saddles and a white underside. This sluggish, bottom-dwelling shark prefers cooler waters and is found close inshore, often on sandy bottoms, to a depth of 40 m. Diet consists of fishes, squid and various crustaceans. An endemic shark, ranging from Cape Town to Durban. These common sharks have a curious habit of curling up when disturbed.

Leopard shark

Whale shark

Shortnose blacktail reef shark

Whitetip reef shark

Houndshark

Puffadder shyshark

PYJAMA SHARK (STRIPED CATSHARK) – *Poroderma africanum*
Attains 100 cm. Identified by seven longitudinal black stripes on upper body. Background colour is grey to creamy brown. This species has a flat head with a blunt snout and short nasal barbels. Nocturnal, resting on the seabed, in caves or below overhangs during the day. Inhabits both inshore and offshore reefs to a depth of 100 m. Preys on various crustaceans and fish. This endemic species is found only between the southern Western Cape and East London. It is harmless and common.

Hammerhead sharks – Family Sphyrnidae

SCALLOPED HAMMERHEAD – *Sphyrna lewini*
Attains 320 cm. Identified by distinctive hammer-shaped head, with eyes situated on lateral extensions. Has a scalloped snout, which is concave at the centre. The overall colour is grey to bronze dorsally and white ventrally. Ranges from surface waters down to depths of 250 m. Preys on fish, small sharks and crayfish (rocklobster). Worldwide distribution in temperate and tropical waters, occurring as far south as the Eastern Cape. Immature scalloped hammerheads are common along the KwaZulu-Natal coast and are sometimes encountered in large shoals near the surface. Generally timid. Similar to the smooth hammerhead shark, which also has a scalloped snout, but which is convex at the centre.

RAYS

Rays have cartilaginous skeletons and flattened bodies. Greatly expanded pectoral fins are fused to the head, giving them a disc-like shape. Five to six gill slits occur on the underside of the head. Spiracles (nostrils) are located dorsally, behind the eyes. Many have a whip-like tail, armed with one or two sharp barbs, which are used for defence. Rays are not aggressive, and retaliate only if provoked. Guitarfishes (sandsharks) exhibit features of both sharks and rays. They have a flat body with expanded pectoral fins and a well-developed tail. Rays and guitarfishes have minute flattened teeth arranged diagonally in pavement fashion, which are used for crushing hard-shelled prey. Most rays and guitarfishes inhabit sandy or muddy bottoms.

Guitarfishes (sandsharks) – Family Rhinobatidae

BOWMOUTH GUITARFISH – *Rhina ancylostoma*
Attains 240 cm. Prehistoric in appearance with its broad, rounded snout, wing-like pectoral fins and ridges of thorn-like protuberances over head and back. The upper surface is grey or brownish with scattered spots. The underside is pale. Usually occurs inshore over sand and rubble areas, but is also found down to depths of 90 m. Preys on crustaceans and shelled invertebrates. Extends throughout tropical Indo-West Pacific, south to KwaZulu-Natal but is rarely seen by divers.

GIANT GUITARFISH – *Rhynchobatus djiddensis*
Attains 310 cm. Largest of the guitarfish family, best recognized by its elongated snout, black eye-spots on pectoral bases and the lunate-shaped tail. Colour ranges from khaki to dark brown, with lines of white spots on upper surface. Spots not always present, especially in large adults. The underside is white. It inhabits sandy areas from the surf-zone down to 50 m, preying on bivalve molluscs, crabs and small fish. Widespread throughout the Red Sea, tropical western Indian Ocean and south to the Eastern Cape. Common off KwaZulu-Natal during summer. Considered a prize fish by anglers.

Eaglerays – Family Myliobatidae

BULLRAY (EAGLERAY) – *Myliobatis aquila*
Attains a disc width of 150 cm. Has a raised head and short rounded snout. Colour is uniform chocolate-brown dorsally, and white ventrally. Sometimes occurs in groups, and may occasionally leap out of the water. Frequents sandy shores, lagoons and estuaries, as well as offshore areas down to 95 m. Feeds on bivalves, crabs, fish and squid. Ranges from the Mediterranean Sea, eastern Atlantic, around the Cape, to KwaZulu-Natal. More common in temperate waters.

SPOTTED EAGLERAY – *Aetobatus narinari*
Attains a disc width of 220 cm. Numerous small, white spots mark the dark brown or black upper surface. Underside is white. Has a distinctive duckbill snout and a whip-like tail, which may be 2,5 times as long as the body. Has the ability to leap out of the water. Usually solitary, but may form small groups. Often found patrolling reefs. Ranges in depth from 1-50 m. Feeds mainly on bivalves, crabs, shrimps and octopus. Found in most tropical seas, ranging south to the Eastern Cape. An uncommon species.

Pyjama shark

Scalloped hammerhead

Bowmouth guitarfish

Giant guitarfish

Bullray

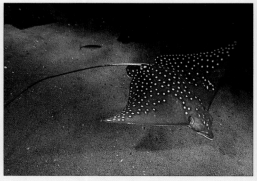

Spotted eagleray

Stingrays – Family Dasyatidae

BLUESPOTTED STINGRAY – *Dasyatis kuhlii*
Attains a disc width of 70 cm. Distinctive kite-shaped stingray with small vivid blue spots on a reddish-brown background, and a white underside. The tail has black and white bands behind the barb. Favours sandy and rocky habitats and is often found partly covered by sand on the seabed or under ledges, when not actively hunting for prey. Ranges in depth from 3-90 m. Diet consists mainly of shrimps and crabs. Widespread throughout Indo-West Pacific. A reasonably common species between Durban and southern Mozambique.

BLUE STINGRAY – *Dasyatis chrysonota*
Attains a disc width of 75 cm. The upper surface has irregular blue markings on a golden brown background. The underside is white. The tail is less than twice the body length and usually has only one barb. During summer, migrations from offshore to sheltered sandy bays occur. Often buries itself under a thin layer of sand when resting. Found in depths from 3-50 m. Feeds on small fish, shrimps and crabs. Ranges from West Africa, Namibia to KwaZulu-Natal. This stingray prefers cooler temperate waters. A common species.

SHARPNOSED STINGRAY (BROWN STINGRAY) – *Himantura gerrardi*
Attains a disc width of 90 cm. Medium-sized stingray with a pointed snout. The tail is twice as long as the body. Uniform light brown colour above, and white on underside. Tail of juveniles is marked with light and dark brown bands. Occurs along sandy shores, in shallow bays and estuaries, to a depth of 50 m. Preys on bottom-dwelling crustaceans such as shrimps, crabs and crayfish (rocklobster). Ranges throughout Indo-West Pacific, south to the Eastern Cape. A common species.

HONEYCOMB STINGRAY – *Himantura uarnak*
Attains a disc width of 200 cm. This large ray is unmistakable with its pale brown, honeycomb pattern on a brown background, and white underside. Juveniles are pale brown with small dark spots. Has a pointed snout and a very long tail, up to 3 times longer than the body. Often buries itself under the sand, with only the eyes and tail visible. Found in estuaries and sandy areas near reefs to a depth of 50 m. Diet consists of molluscs, crustaceans and squid. Widespread throughout Indo-West Pacific, south to the Eastern Cape. A reasonably common species.

BONY FISH

Moray Eels – Family Muraenidae
Moray eels are slender, snake-like fish, which lack scales, as well as pelvic and pectoral fins. They constantly open and close their large mouth to move water over their gills for respiration, and have sharp, pointed teeth. Most are secretive during the day, hiding in recesses in the reef, with only their heads protruding. They are voracious nocturnal hunters of small fish and octopus, and detect their prey by smell. Although generally not aggressive towards divers, they can inflict a nasty bite if provoked.

RIBBON EEL – *Rhinomuraena quaesita*
Attains 120 cm. This colourful moray eel has a long, slender, ribbon-like body and a small head with funnel-shaped 'flaps' on the nostrils, and fleshy barbels at the end of the lower jaw. Adult males are brilliant blue, with a yellow snout, lower jaw and dorsal fin. Mature females are almost entirely yellow. Juveniles and sub-adults up to about 65 cm in length are black, with a yellow dorsal fin. The ribbon eel is capable of changing sex and coloration. Usually lives in a small sand-burrow at the base of coral or rocky reefs. Ranges in depth from 1-55 m. Feeds mainly on small fishes. Widespread throughout Indo-Pacific, south to KwaZulu-Natal. Uncommon and seldom seen by divers.

Bluespotted stingray

Blue stingray

Sharpnosed stingray

Honeycomb stingray

Ribbon eel (male)

Ribbon eel (juvenile)

ZEBRA MORAY – *Gymnomuraena zebra*
Attains at least 100 cm. Dark brown to black in colour, with distinctive narrow white rings around head and along body. Teeth are close-set and pebble-like, with no sharp fangs. Ranges from rocky shores to offshore reefs at depths between 1-40 m. Feeds on crustaceans and other small reef animals. Occurs throughout Indo-West Pacific and tropical eastern Pacific, south to KwaZulu-Natal. A secretive and rather docile moray eel.

SALT AND PEPPER MORAY – *Gymnothorax eurostus*
Attains 57 cm. Colour variable but usually purplish brown, with numerous yellow specks densely scattered anteriorly and sparsely on the tail region. Found on inshore and offshore reefs at depths of 1-25 m. Feeds mainly on fishes and crustaceans. Occurs throughout Indo-Pacific, south to the Eastern Cape. A relatively common, yet rarely observed species.

LEOPARD MORAY – *Gymnothorax undulatus*
Attains at least 150 cm. Highly variable coloration. Background colour is usually pale yellow, densely mottled with irregular brown or bluish-grey markings. Inhabits rocky shores and offshore reefs to a depth of 30 m. Often found on shipwrecks. Hunts mainly at night, preying on small fish and octopuses. Widespread throughout Indo-Pacific, and very common from the Eastern Cape to southern Mozambique. Can be aggressive to divers if provoked.

GIANT MORAY – *Gymnothorax javanicus*
Attains 300 cm but 240 cm is more common. Largest of its kind in the Indian Ocean. Distinguished by its size, heavy-set appearance, and small dark spots on top of the head and back. Body colour is uniform light brown to tan, with a black patch at the gill openings. Occurs in a variety of reef habitats, ranging from the intertidal zone to depths of at least 50 m. Preys mainly on fish and crustaceans. Found throughout Indo-Pacific, extending south to central Mozambique. This common species is normally docile, but is capable of inflicting injury to divers if provoked.

Snake eels – Family Ophichthidae

Snake eels are a large and diverse group. Their bodies are almost round in cross section, scaleless, and most have prominent snouts with downward pointing nostrils. They spend much of the time buried under the sand near reefs, but are occasionally seen moving slowly across the seabed. Interestingly, they can move around beneath the sand. They prey on small fish and crustaceans using their acute sense of smell. Often mistaken for sea snakes, but they lack scales and the flattened paddle-like tail characteristic of sea snakes.

OCELLATED SNAKE-EEL (SPOTTED SNAKE-EEL) – *Myrichthys maculosus*
Attains 50 cm. Cream in colour, with large and small black oval spots along the body. Occurs on shallow reefs to depths of about 30 m. Sometimes seen moving over sandy or weedy areas. Preys on sand-dwelling fishes and crustaceans. Ranges from Indo-Pacific south to the Eastern Cape. This uncommon species is harmless to divers.

Conger eels – Family Congridae

This family includes garden eels and conger eels. Garden eels have very slender round bodies with tiny pectoral fins. They usually form large colonies on sand-flats and slopes where they live in individual tube-like burrows. The tail is secured in the burrow whilst the rest of the body protrudes freely outside, moving in a graceful wave-like motion to catch zooplankton. When threatened, they retreat into their burrows. Garden eels rarely leave their home and are extremely shy, and are thus very difficult to approach underwater.

SPOTTED GARDEN-EEL – *Heteroconger hassi*
Attains 40 cm. The body is white, with numerous small black spots. Two large black spots mark its sides, one just behind the gill opening and the other further along the body. This species is found in sandy areas exposed to currents in depths of 15-40 m. Feeds on zooplankton. Widespread throughout Indo-Pacific, extending to northern Kwa-Zulu Natal. An uncommon and very shy species.

Zebra moray

Salt and pepper moray

Leopard moray

Giant moray

Ocellated snake-eel

Spotted garden-eel

Eel Catfishes – Family Plotosidae

Catfishes are characterized by a slender, tapering eel-like body with barbels around the mouth. Venomous spines are located at the front of the pectoral fins and the first dorsal fin.

STRIPED EEL CATFISH – *Plotosus lineatus*

Attains 32 cm. Two white lateral stripes mark the sides of the black body. The black fades to brown with age. Adults are solitary and hide by day. Juveniles may form dense shoals for protection against predation. Frequents estuaries, tidal pools and reefs to a depth of 35 m. Feeds at night on bottom-dwelling invertebrates. Widespread throughout Indo-West Pacific, south to Eastern Cape. Reasonably common.

Lizardfishes – Family Synodontidae

Lizardfish are moderately small, cylindrically shaped, bottom-dwelling fish. They are recognized by their reptile-like head and large mouth, which is filled with slender, pointed fangs. These voracious predators lie on the seabed, ready to dart forward and grab passing prey, such as fish and swimming invertebrates.

BLACKTAIL LIZARDFISH – *Synodus jaculum*

Attains 20 cm. Recognized by the large black blotch at tail base and the black marking on snout. Body has irregular vertical dark bars and stripes. Dorsal surface is bluish green. Can pale or darken to suit surroundings. Occurs on coral and rocky reefs to depths of 2-90 m. Preys on fishes and invertebrates. Ranges from Indo-West Pacific, south to southern KwaZulu-Natal. An uncommon species.

Anglerfishes (frogfishes) – Family Antennariidae

These oddly shaped fish have globular, compressed bodies with loose, prickly skin and limb-like pectoral fins. They have a large, upwardly directed mouth. First dorsal spine is modified into a retractable 'fishing rod', tipped with an enticing lure. They lie in wait on the reef, moving the lure to attract prey, which is swallowed whole. They are masters at camouflage, as body colour and skin texture blend into the background.

GIANT ANGLERFISH – *Antennarius commerson*

Attains 33 cm. Colour ranges from beige, black, yellow, green to orange. Adults mimic sponges perfectly. Found on coral reefs in depths of 1-45 m. Feeds on fish and crustaceans. Widespread throughout Indo-West Pacific, Red Sea, extending to KwaZulu-Natal. An uncommon to rare species.

PAINTED ANGLERFISH – *Antennarius pictus*

Attains 25 cm. Generally mottled yellow, brown and pink with irregular dark and white patches. Has numerous skin flaps and filamentous appendages on body and head. Found on coral and rocky offshore reefs to a depth of 40 m. Preys on fish and crustaceans. Occurs throughout tropical Indo-West Pacific, extending to southern KwaZulu-Natal. Uncommon and seldom sighted due to its excellent camouflage.

Needlefishes – Family Belonidae

Needlefish (garfish) have elongated, slender bodies and an extended mouth with rows of needle-like teeth. Their blue-green back and silvery sides helps them blend into the open surface waters, thereby avoiding detection by predators. Preys on pelagic fishes. Able to skip along the surface on their tails if threatened.

CROCODILE NEEDLEFISH – *Tylosurus crocodilus crocodilus*

Attains 130 cm. Silvery with a blue-green back and a faint blue stripe along the side of body. Inhabits coastal waters and estuaries in depths from 0.2-5 m. Feeds on small pelagic fishes. Widely distributed throughout the Atlantic and Indo-West Pacific Ocean, south to KwaZulu-Natal. A common species.

Berycids – Family Berycidae

Berycids occur worldwide, except for the eastern Pacific Ocean. They are small to medium-sized fish with large eyes and generally occur in deep water. In some areas they are caught commercially.

SHORT ALFONSINO – *Centroberyx spinosus*

Attains 20 cm. Distinguished by a deep body profile, large eyes, reddish-orange head and upper body, and golden sides. Tail has a prominent pale blue bar. Usually observed drifting close to caves and overhangs during the day. Inhabits offshore reefs in depths of 30-60 m. Occurs singly or in small groups. A nocturnal feeder of crustaceans and small fish. An endemic species, known only from the Storms River in the Western Cape to Durban. Relatively common on the deeper reefs off southern KwaZulu-Natal.

Striped eel catfish

Blacktail lizardfish

Giant anglerfish

Painted anglerfish

Crocodile needlefish

Short Alfonsino

Squirrelfishes and soldierfishes – Family Holocentridae

Squirrelfish and soldierfish are medium-sized fish, usually with reddish, oblong bodies and large, squirrel-like eyes. The scales are large and rough, and the fins very spiny. Many species are similar in appearance. The distinguishing feature between the two groups is a large, sharp, defensive spine, which is found at the base of the gill plate in squirrelfish. They generally shelter in or lurk close to caves, under ledges, or among dense coral growth during the day, emerging at night to hunt for prey.

SILVER SQUIRRELFISH (CLEARFIN SQUIRRELFISH) – *Neoniphon argenteus*

Attains 25 cm. The body is silvery with rows of horizontal, reddish-brown, dotted stripes on sides, and a clear dorsal fin. Usually observed in small groups, drifting near coral heads. Inhabits sheltered coral reefs to a depth of at least 20 m, feeding mainly on crustaceans. More abundant on oceanic islands and ranges from the Indo-West Pacific, south to Mozambique. A relatively common species.

BIGSCALE SOLDIER – *Myripristis berndti*

Attains 30 cm. Recognized by silvery-pink scales with red edges, giving it an overall pale reddish appearance. The first dorsal fin is yellow while the median fins have red and white leading edges. Shelters below overhangs in small groups during the day. Found in relatively shallow water on coral and rocky reefs at depths of 3-30 m. Feeds on zooplankton at night. Widespread throughout Indo-Pacific and tropical eastern Pacific, south to KwaZulu-Natal. A common species that may be confused with the blotcheye soldier, *Myripristis murdjan*, which is darker red in colour and has a red tipped first dorsal fin.

YELLOWFIN SOLDIER – *Myripristis chryseres*

Attains 25 cm. Uniform red colour with bright yellow median and pelvic fins. Encountered singly, or occasionally in small groups beneath overhangs or in caves during the daytime. Rarely found in depths less than 25 m. It feeds on zooplankton at night. The yellowfin soldier occurs in limited areas of the Indo-Pacific, extending to southern KwaZulu-Natal and is an uncommon species.

LATTICE SOLDIER (VIOLET SOLDIER) – *Myripristis violacea*

Attains 25 cm. Overall silvery-blue colour with dark-rimmed scales. The gill opening has a reddish-brown bar, and the median fins have white leading edges with pale red tips. Found on shallow protected coral reefs to a depth of 25 m. A nocturnal feeder of zooplankton. Widespread throughout Indo-Pacific. Not often encountered in South African waters, but moderately common in tropical areas.

IMMACULATE SOLDIER (WHITE-TIPPED SOLDIERFISH) – *Myripristis vittata*

Attains 20 cm. Body colour is uniform reddish-orange, with white tipped dorsal spines and white leading edges on median and pelvic fins. Lacks the dark bar at the gill opening. Often forms sizeable groups in or near caves and overhangs by day. Sometimes seen swimming inverted on a cave roof. Encountered on offshore reefs at depths between 10-80 m. Diet consists mainly of large zooplankton, such as crab larvae. Widespread throughout Indo-Pacific, south to KwaZulu-Natal. One of the most common soldierfish throughout its range.

EPAULETTE SOLDIERFISH (PEARLY SOLDIERFISH) – *Myripristis kuntee*

Attains 20 cm. Distinguished by its pale colour with a pearly sheen, and its relatively small scales. Has a prominent dark bar at the gill-opening and the dorsal spine tips are yellow. Ranges from rocky shores to offshore reefs in depths to at least 35 m. Usually forms groups that hover in front of caves and near crevices by day, dispersing at night to feed on zooplankton. Occurs throughout Indo-Pacific, extending to KwaZulu-Natal. Very common on northern KwaZulu-Natal reefs.

Silver squirrelfish

Bigscale soldier

Yellowfin soldier

Lattice soldier

Immaculate soldier

Epaulette soldierfish

Pipefishes – Family Syngnathidae

These small fish are relatives of the seahorse. Characterized by a long, slender body, which is encased in rings of bony plates, and an extended tubular snout. Reproduction is unique as males incubate the eggs. The female deposits her eggs in the ventral pouch of the male, where they are embedded into the skin and fertilized. The pregnant male carries the eggs until hatching occurs. Species are seldom seen by divers due to their excellent camouflage.

BANDED PIPEFISH (RINGED PIPEFISH) – *Dunckerocampus boylei*
Attains 16 cm. Striking red and white bands occur along the body. They have been observed to act as cleaners, removing small parasites from fishes. Often swim upside down. Usually found in pairs hovering in deep caves at depths greater than 15 m. Feeds on small invertebrates. Known only from KwaZulu-Natal, Mauritius, Red Sea and Indonesia. This rare species has only recently been described.

RED-SCRIBBLED PIPEFISH – *Corythoichthys* sp.
Attains 10 cm. Has red spots on short snout, and regularly spaced, brown-red bands along pale body. Small, pale spots with dark edges are present on bands. Found in rubble areas adjacent to reefs. Adults occur in pairs ranging in depth from 15-25 m. Feeds on small invertebrates. A western Indian Ocean species, extending to northern KwaZulu-Natal. Uncommon and easily overlooked. Possibly undescribed.

Ghost pipefishes – Family Solenostomidae

Ghost pipefish are related to true pipefish. The body is encased in segmented bony plates. Pelvic fins are large, and the snout elongate. Unlike pipefish, females incubate fertilized eggs in a pouch. Masters of camouflage.

GHOST PIPEFISH – *Solenostomus cyanopterus*
Attains 16 cm. Colour varies from light green to dark brown, sometimes with a scattering of black and white spots. Mimics floating seaweed to avoid detection. Often found in pairs on inshore and offshore reefs to a depth of 30 m. Drifts over seabed, often in a head-down position, searching for small invertebrate prey. Distributed throughout Indo-Pacific, south to the Eastern Cape. An uncommon species.

Shrimpfishes (razorfishes) – Family Centriscidae

Shrimpfishes are related to pipefish and seahorses. The body is flattened and covered with bony plates. Has an elongated tubular snout and a ventral keel. Drifts head-down over seabed in synchronized groups.

SPECKLED SHRIMPFISH – *Aeoliscus punctulatus*
Attains 20 cm. Almost transparent with a mid-lateral brown stripe from tip of snout to tail. Tiny black spots are scattered over head and body. Found near areas of rich plant or coral growth. Depth varies from 2-40 m. Feeds on zooplankton and tiny invertebrates, which are drawn in through its small mouth. Confined to Red Sea and western Indian Ocean, south to the Eastern Cape. An uncommon species.

Scorpionfishes – Family Scorpaenidae

Includes several subfamilies of which lionfishes (Pteroinae) and the scorpionfishes (Scorpaenidae) are the most common. The majority possesses venomous spines. The spectacular lionfishes are nocturnal hunters and have long dorsal fin spines and enlarged pectoral fins. Scorpionfishes are bottom-dwelling fishes with excellent camouflage. They lie motionless in ambush for prey. Some are potentially dangerous.

RADIAL FIREFISH (CLEARFIN LIONFISH) – *Pterois radiata*
Attains 20 cm. Body colour is dark red with thin white bars along body, and prominent white pectoral fin rays. Unique horizontal white lines on base of the tail, and unmarked pectoral fin membranes. Inhabits inshore and offshore reefs, ranging in depth from 3-25 m. Juveniles sometimes occur in tidal pools. Tends to hide in crevices by day, coming out at night to prey on small fishes and shrimps. Occurs throughout Indo-Pacific, extending to southern KwaZulu-Natal. An uncommon species.

FALSE STONEFISH (DEVIL SCORPIONFISH) – *Scorpaenopsis diabolus*
Attains 22 cm. Distinguished by its humped back, and orange, black and white colours on inner side of pectoral fins. Body colour resembles dead coral, and is usually mottled grey to white, with irregular brown to reddish blotches. Inhabits rubble or weedy bottoms of tropical lagoons and offshore reefs, to a depth of 70 m. Preys on small fishes and invertebrates. Widespread throughout Indo-West Pacific, Red Sea, and south to KwaZulu-Natal. A relatively uncommon species. Resembles the true stonefish.

Banded pipefish

Red-scribbled pipefish

Ghost pipefish

Speckled shrimpfish

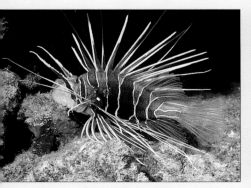

Radial firefish

False stonefish

TASSELED SCORPIONFISH (SMALL SCALE SCORPIONFISH) – *Scorpaenopsis oxycephala*
Attains 35 cm. One of the largest members of the scorpionfish family. This species has a more depressed head and a greater number of branched tentacles and skin filaments over body and head in comparison to related species. Has a generally frilly appearance. Coloration is mottled red-brown to bright red. Found on coral and rocky reefs from the shallows to a depth of 35 m. Preys on fishes and invertebrates. Widespread throughout Indo-Pacific, Red Sea, south to northern KwaZulu-Natal. Relatively common. Similar to the raggy scorpionfish, *Scorpaenopsis venosa*, which is less frilly in appearance.

MAURITIUS SCORPIONFISH – *Rhinopias eschmeyeri*
Attains 19 cm. Coloration varies from light blue to pink and yellow. Body is deep and laterally compressed, and lacks filaments and markings. A prominent fleshy flap is located above both eyes, which are set high up on the head. Inhabits coral and rocky reefs and weedy areas in depths of 3-40 m. Lies motionless in wait for fish and invertebrate prey. Ranges throughout western Indian Ocean, south to KwaZulu-Natal. Considered rare and is often overlooked due to its camouflage.

Flatheads – Family Platycephalidae

The flathead family is distinguished by a flattened head and large mouth, with the lower jaw longer than the upper jaw. The depressed body tapers towards the tail. They are closely related to scorpionfish. Both groups have bony ridges and short spines on the head. Flatheads are well-camouflaged, bottom-dwelling fish that generally live on sandy and muddy bottoms. They partially bury themselves to ambush passing prey. Many species are similar in appearance, making identification difficult.

LONGHEAD FLATHEAD (INDIAN OCEAN CROCODILEFISH) – *Papilloculiceps longiceps*
Attains 70 cm. Commonly known as a crocodilefish. Upper body surface is well camouflaged with mottled brownish or greenish patterns. Interesting features are the lace-like lappets, which camouflage and protect the eyes. Usually found lying on the reef or adjacent sandy areas in depths of 1-30 m. Preys on fishes and crustaceans. Widespread in western Indian Ocean, extending from KwaZulu-Natal to the Red Sea. One of the most common flatheads.

BARTAIL FLATHEAD – *Platycephalus indicus*
Attains 100 cm. Generally brownish or greyish with a sandy pattern above, and a white underside. Identified by the horizontal white and black stripes on tail, with a yellow centre. Inhabits sandy and muddy areas, from estuaries to inshore reefs and bays, down to a depth of 25 m. Inconspicuous due to coloration. An aggressive predator, often taken by anglers. Widespread throughout Indo-West Pacific and the Red Sea, extending to the southern Western Cape. Common along the east coast of southern Africa.

Gurnards – Family Triglidae

Gurnards are bottom-dwelling fish, characterized by large, colourful wing-like pectoral fins, which can be flared to deter would-be predators. The lower three fin-rays are free and enlarged, and are used for 'walking' on the seabed, and as feelers when searching for food. They have an elongated body, which tapers towards the tail. The head is encased in an armour of bony plates. They lie motionless on the seabed, ready to pounce on passing prey.

BLUEFIN GURNARD – *Chelidonichthys kumu*
Attains 60 cm. Brownish to red upper body, and pale underside. The colourful pectoral fins are dark blue-green, with blue edging and a black patch overlaid with bluish-white spots near the base of the fin. Ranges from rocky shores to offshore reefs in depths of 1-200 m. Feeds mainly on bottom-dwelling crustaceans. Widespread throughout Indo-West Pacific. Occurs in southern Africa between Cape Town and Maputo. This moderately common species is commercially exploited by inshore trawl-fishery. The Cape gurnard, *Chelidonichthys capensis*, is very similar, but does not have the blue edging to the pectoral fins.

BLUEWING GURNARD – *Chelidonichthys* sp.
Attains 60 cm. Thought to be a new species, remains to be described. Body is mottled with red, brown and white markings. Top of head is often mauve in colour. Pectoral fins have spectacular bright blue markings on a green background. Observed lying on rocky reefs at depths greater than 25 m. Preys mainly on crustaceans. Recorded off southern KwaZulu-Natal and Eastern Cape coasts. Possibly has much wider distribution. A relatively uncommon species.

Tasseled scorpionfish

Mauritius scorpionfish

Longhead flathead

Bartail flathead

Bluefin gurnard

Bluewing gurnard

Rockcods – Family Serranidae

Rockcods, also known as groupers, vary considerably in size and are characterized by their strong, robust bodies, rounded pectoral fins and large mouths. Many commence maturity as females but change sex later in life. They are solitary, carnivorous reef-dwellers, spending much of the day lurking in caves or under ledges. Prey is drawn whole into their gullets by powerful suction created when they suddenly open their large mouths. Many of these nocturnal predators are strongly territorial and inquisitive. Some of the larger species are important to the line-fishery and are extremely susceptible to over exploitation.

KOESTER – *Acanthistius sebastoides*

Attains 35 cm. This small rockcod has a robust body, small scales and a large mouth. The upper body is reddish brown with distinctive white blotches, and the underside is white. A solitary fish found among rocks on both inshore and offshore reefs, ranging in depth from 1-40 m. Preys on small fish and crabs. Endemic to southern Africa, where it is particularly common along the coast of the Eastern Cape and southern KwaZulu-Natal.

Subfamily Anthiinae

ONE-STRIPE ANTHIAS – *Pseudanthias fasciatus*

Attains 21 cm. This striking species is the largest of the 'goldie' family. Females have a yellow body with a distinctive red lateral stripe, edged in white. Males lack this stripe and have a large reddish patch at the rear of the head. Males form harems and exhibit courtship behaviour. Often swims upside down below overhangs. Occurs in groups in or near caves and under ledges in depths of 35-80 m. Feeds exclusively on zooplankton. Widespread throughout Indo-West Pacific, Red Sea, south to KwaZulu-Natal. Rarely seen in South African waters due to its deep water habitat; however sometimes sighted on the northern pinnacles of Protea Banks, off southern KwaZulu-Natal at depths of around 35 m.

Subfamily Epinephelinae

SLENDER ROCKCOD – *Anyperodon leucogrammicus*

Attains 52 cm. As the common name suggests, the body is noticeably elongate and the head is pointed. General colour is greenish to brownish grey, with numerous orange-red spots located in rows on head and body. Four longitudinal whitish streaks, which disappear with age, occur on the sides. A secretive, solitary species, usually found on sheltered coral reefs in depths of 5-80 m. Feeds primarily on small fishes. Widespread throughout tropical Indo-West Pacific, Red Sea, south to central Mozambique. An uncommon species.

TOMATO ROCKCOD – *Cephalopholis sonnerati*

Attains 57 cm. A medium-sized rockcod, recognized by its deep, compressed body and slightly concave head profile. Colour varies from brilliant red to brownish grey, with large white spots scattered on head, body and fins, but not on pectoral fins. Capable of changing colour dramatically from red to brown to tan, as shown in the photographs opposite. Usually solitary, but sometimes found in small groups. This rockcod is often associated with isolated reefs on open bottoms. Inhabits coral and rocky reefs, ranging in depth from 12-100 m. Preys on small fish and crustaceans. Ranges from western Indian Ocean to the central Pacific, extending to southern KwaZulu-Natal. One of the more common species found on southern African east coast reefs.

Koester

One-stripe anthias (female)

One stripe anthias (male)

Slender rockcod

Tomato rockcod (red form)

Tomato rockcod (grey form)

MARBLED ROCKCOD – *Epinephelus polyphekadion*
Attains 65 cm. Main distinguishing features are a prominent black saddle on the base of the tail and two black spots on the tip of the snout. Head and body are light brown and covered with large, irregular brown blotches, overlaid by numerous small brown spots. Usually found in coral rich areas of tropical lagoons and sheltered reefs. Ranges in depth from 3-50 m. Feeds primarily on crustaceans and occasionally on fishes. Widespread throughout Indo-Pacific, Red Sea, south to Mozambique. Moderately common and easily approachable. Often confused with the similar brown marbled rockcod, *Epinephelus fuscoguttatus*, which has a more yellowish-brown ground colour and an indented head profile.

CATFACE ROCKCOD – *Epinephelus andersoni*
Attains 80 cm. The body is robust and moderately elongated. Colour ranges from brown to grey. Numerous dark brown spots cover the body and extend onto the tail and dorsal fins. Three distinctive oblique black stripes usually occur across the head. Sometimes a line of white spots is present along the back, especially in juveniles. Frequents inshore and offshore rocky reefs down to at least 50 m. Often seen resting on the reef, ready to ambush prey such as fishes, crabs and crayfish (rocklobsters). Known only from the southern Eastern Cape to southern Mozambique. An important species in the KwaZulu-Natal line-fishery. Very common in southern African waters.

BROWNSPOTTED ROCKCOD – *Epinephelus chlorostigma*
Attains 75 cm. Body is pale brown with dark brown, close-set hexagonal spots extending onto the fins. Spots are larger than the space between them. The rear edge of the tail has a narrow white margin. Inhabits coral and rocky reefs, and seagrass beds. More common on moderately deep reefs. Ranges in depth from 4-150 m. Diet consists of fish, crabs and squid. Widespread throughout Indo-West Pacific, Red Sea, south to KwaZulu-Natal. A common species that is similar to the squaretail rockcod, *Epinephelus areolatus*, which is also spotted, but with larger, wider spaced pale yellow spots.

WHITESPOTTED ROCKCOD – *Epinephelus caeruleopunctatus*
Attains 60 cm. Body colour ranges from dark blue to grey-brown, with large white spots mixed with numerous small pale spots scattered over the body. The head is pointed. The rear half of the tail is black with no spots. Generally stays close to caves or crevices in the reef by day. Inhabits coral and rocky reefs at depths of 4-65 m. Feeds on fishes and crustaceans. Widespread in western Indian Ocean, south to the Eastern Cape and east to Japan and Australia. A relatively common rockcod.

MALABAR ROCKCOD – *Epinephelus malabaricus*
Attains 150 cm. Overall colour is pale grey to brown or olive. Several irregular dark, oblique bands, pale spots, blotches and small dark spots mark the body. Tends to be strongly territorial and solitary. Its mottled colour provides excellent camouflage in the shadows below overhangs and inside caves. Found in various habitats including estuaries, channels, rocky shores and offshore reefs down to at least 60 m. Feeds on fishes and crustaceans, such as crayfish (rocklobster) and crabs. Ranges from the western Pacific to East Africa, Red Sea, south to the Eastern Cape. A relatively common species that is generally wary and difficult to approach. Similar to the orange-spotted rockcod, *Epinephelus coioides*, which has small orange spots on body and fins and yellow outer edges to the median and pectoral fins.

TIGER ROCKCOD (STRIPED-FIN ROCKCOD) – *Epinephelus posteli*
Attains 100 cm. This distinctive rockcod has a slender body, covered with small, close-set irregular reddish-brown spots with pale spaces between the spots. From a distance, the overall colour appears red with dark spots. Sometimes four narrow, oblique pale bars appear on the rear of the body, depending on the behavioural mood. Frequents coral reefs ranging in depth from 5-50 m. Often rests on the reef, ready to ambush small fish and crustaceans. Known only from Madagascar, Mozambique and KwaZulu-Natal. Considered an uncommon species but is usually quite approachable.

Marbled rockcod

Catface rockcod

Brownspotted rockcod

Whitespotted rockcod

Malabar rockcod

Tiger rockcod

GREASY ROCKCOD – *Epinephelus tauvina*
Attains 70 cm. The head, body and fins are pale grey, and covered with well-spaced, dull orange-red to red-brown spots. Five faint oblique dark bars may be present on the body. Usually a blackish blotch occurs at the base of the spinous dorsal fin. Often observed lying on or next to reefs waiting to ambush passing prey. Found at depths of 1-50 m. Feeds mainly on fish and occasionally on crustaceans. Widespread throughout Indo-Pacific, Red Sea, south to northern KwaZulu-Natal. A moderately common species.

Subfamily Serraninae

COMBER – *Serranus cabrilla*
Attains 30 cm. The comber has a distinctive colour pattern. The head and upper body are brown, whilst the remainder of body is white with two slightly irregular, longitudinal brown stripes from head to tail. Sometimes has several short dark brown bars on body. This solitary fish inhabits rocky reefs from the shore down to depths of 200 m. Preys on fishes and crustaceans. Ranges from Mediterranean Sea, eastern Atlantic Ocean and around the South African coast to KwaZulu-Natal. Relatively uncommon.

Subfamily Grammistidae

Soapfish are closely related to rockcods. They are a group of fishes that release a slimy layer of a bitter toxin, known as grammistin, from the skin when stressed in order to deter would-be predators.

GOLDRIBBON SOAPFISH – *Aulacocephalus temmincki*
Attains 35 cm. Overall body colour is deep blue with a bright yellow band from the snout along the back to the tail. Inhabits rocky reefs, ranging in depth from 20-120 m. Usually found at depths greater than 30 m. This soapfish generally stays close to caves and crevices and feeds primarily on fishes and shrimps. Primarily sub-tropical, widespread throughout Indo-Pacific, extending to southern KwaZulu-Natal. An uncommon and shy species, only occasionally encountered when it ventures out from its shelter.

Dottybacks – Family Pseudochromidae

Dottybacks are small, slender and often brilliantly coloured fishes that are cryptic inhabitants of crevices and holes in the reef. They are also highly territorial and can be aggressive. The female deposits a ball of eggs on the reef, which is guarded by the male.

NATAL DOTTYBACK – *Pseudochromis natalensis*
Attains 9 cm. This inconspicuous but curious dottyback has an overall olive colour with a small blue spot on each scale. Generally a solitary species, but occasionally occurs in pairs. It never strays far from its shelter. Inhabits offshore reefs and is usually found on or along reef edges, particularly in rubble and weedy areas, at depths of between 10-30 m. Feeds on small invertebrates and zooplankton. Ranges from southern KwaZulu-Natal, to Kenya and Madagascar. Common along the KwaZulu-Natal coast.

DARK DOTTYBACK – *Pseudochromis melas*
Attains 9 cm. Two different colour variations occur: one is uniform dark blue, the other comprises a dark blue head and back with pale yellow sides and a yellow tail. The latter colour form is similar to *Pseudochromis pesi*, which has whitish sides, a black upper head and back, and a yellow tail. Both colour forms have an elongated royal blue spot on the upper gill cover edged in yellow. Inhabits the base of seaward reefs, particularly in flat areas with mixed sand and rock. Usually solitary, it remains close to shelter. Found in depths of 25-40 m, where it feeds on zooplankton and small invertebrates. Ranges from northern KwaZulu-Natal to Kenya. An uncommon species.

Thornfishes – Family Teraponidae

Most species of thornfish live in shallow coastal and brackish waters, some even in fresh water. They are small, slightly oblong fish with spines on the head and the dorsal fin. Most are silvery with brown or blackish stripes. They usually have a shoaling habit.

THORNFISH – *Terapon jarbua*
Attains 25 cm. Silvery body with three upward carved brown stripes on sides. Inhabits rocky shores and can tolerate brackish water. Juveniles are common in intertidal areas and estuaries. Ranges in depth from 0,3-12 m. Diet includes small crabs, shrimps and fish fry. Also eats scales of other fish. Widespread throughout Indo-West Pacific, south to the eastern Cape. A common species.

Greasy rockcod

Comber

Goldribbon soapfish

Natal dottyback

Dark dottyback

Thornfish

Cardinalfishes – Family Apogonidae

An extensive family of small colourful fish, characterized by two separate dorsal fins, large eyes and distinct stripes or spots. Many similar species complicate identification. They inhabit both coral and rocky reefs, and some frequent tidal pools. They are slow-moving nocturnal feeders, usually hiding in caves or crevices during the day. Occasionally they congregate close to their shelter. Some males incubate the eggs in their mouths.

GOLDEN CAPPED CARDINALFISH – *Archamia bleekeri*

Attains 6 cm. Distinctive semi-transparent, pinkish body with gold markings on snout extending over nape to rear of pectoral fin. A black spot marks the tail base. Found in large aggregations on coral and rocky reefs and shipwrecks ranging in depth from 3-35 m. Feeds on small invertebrates and zooplankton. Known from KwaZulu-Natal, Taiwan and Indonesia and is common off Durban. Previously identified as *Archamia goni*, but recently changed to *Archamia bleekeri*. Similar to the Mozambique cardinalfish, *Archamia mozambiquensis*, which lacks gold markings.

REDBARRED CARDINALFISH (ORANGE-LINED CARDINALFISH) – *Archamia fucata*

Attains 8 cm. General colour is greyish-silver with numerous vertical, narrow orange lines on sides and a black spot at the tail base. Forms dense aggregations next to caves and among branching corals. Lives in sheltered areas of offshore reefs and tropical lagoons ranging in depth from 2-60 m. Feeds on zooplankton. Widely distributed throughout Indo-Pacific, Red Sea, south to northern KwaZulu-Natal. Common.

NINESTRIPE CARDINALFISH (REEF-FLAT CARDINALFISH) – *Apogon taeniophorus*

Attains 8 cm. Has five or six prominent black stripes along a whitish body. Tail spot merges with the mid-lateral stripe. The tail spot is not as distinct as in the broadbanded cardinalfish, *Apogon angustatus*, and the blackbanded cardinalfish, *Apogon cookii*. Inhabits rocky shores and offshore reefs in depths down to 20 m, where it is found near crevices and under ledges. Diet consists of zooplankton, crabs and prawns. Widespread throughout Indo-Pacific, extending to southern KwaZulu-Natal. A relatively common species.

FIVE-LINED CARDINALFISH (SHARPTOOTH CARDINALFISH) – *Cheilodipterus quinquelineatus*

Attains 12 cm. One of the larger cardinalfish. The body is whitish with five narrow black stripes on sides and a bright yellow area with black spot on base of tail. Forms small to large aggregations among corals and rocks. Juveniles often seek refuge among the spines of sea urchins. Habitat ranges from shallow inshore reefs to offshore reefs in depths of 3-30 m. Feeds on small fishes, crustaceans and gastropods. Widespread throughout Indo-Pacific, Red Sea, extending to southern Mozambique. A common species.

Elf – Family Pomatomidae

ELF (SHAD) – *Pomatomus saltatrix*

Attains 100 cm but 40 cm is more common. Family has one genus with a single species. Elongated, silvery body, with a greenish to bluish dorsal sheen. Other features include small scales, a forked tail and a large mouth set with razor sharp teeth. Confined to coastal waters and usually occurs along sandy shores and fringes of inshore reefs. Has strong shoaling behaviour and undertakes migrations each winter from southern Western Cape to KwaZulu-Natal, following the sardine run. Ranges in depth from 2-40 m. Aggressive predators of small fish. Widespread in cooler areas of all oceans, except eastern Pacific. They are the most important species caught by shore anglers along the South African coast.

Rubberlips (sweetlips) and grunters – Family Haemulidae

A family of small to medium-sized fish. They are closely related to and resemble snappers, but differ in having a smaller mouth, thicker lips, smaller teeth and generally more deeply forked tails. Most have distinctive patterns of stripes or bands. Grunters may grind their pharyngeal teeth together after being captured, producing a grunting sound. Some undergo dramatic changes in colour and pattern with growth.

DUSKY RUBBERLIPS – *Plectorhinchus chubbi*

Attains 75 cm. This bronze-grey robust fish lacks characteristic markings. The head profile is rounded. Lips become fleshy with age. Juveniles live in the intertidal zone, often amongst floating seaweed, while adults inhabit inshore and offshore reefs down to 80 m. Often seen shoaling in small compact groups close to the reef. Feeds on bottom-dwelling invertebrates and small fish. Ranges from western Indian Ocean, across to India and south to the Eastern Cape. Very similar in appearance to the sailfin rubberlips, *Diagramma pictum*, which has a steeper head profile and longer caudal peduncle.

Golden capped cardinalfish

Redbarred cardinalfish

Ninestripe cardinalfish

Five-lined cardinalfish

Elf / Shad

Dusky rubberlips

HARRY HOTLIPS (GIBBUS SWEETLIPS) – *Plectorhinchus gibbosus*
Attains 75 cm. Recognized by its deep body profile, which is deepest at the pectoral fins, its steep head profile and the adults' greatly enlarged lips. Uniform dark grey in colour, sometimes with a reddish tinge A solitary species that prefers turbid inshore reefs. Ranges in depths from 2-40 m. Preys on small fish and invertebrates. Widespread throughout Indo-West Pacific, Red Sea, south to KwaZulu-Natal. Seldom seen by divers.

BARRED RUBBERLIPS (RED-LINED SWEETLIPS) – *Plectorhinchus plagiodesmus*
Attains 90 cm. One of the largest of the rubberlip family. Dark grey body with oblique alternating black and orange bars on sides, and huge orange or yellow sponge-like lips. The orange bars disappear when the fish exceeds about 40 cm in size. Often found in large crevices or beneath ledges by day. Adults occur singly or in small groups. Frequents turbid waters of tropical lagoons, mangroves and offshore coral reefs to depths of between 2-25 m. Feeds on small fish and bottom-dwelling invertebrates at night. Ranges from Somalia to Madagascar, south to northern KwaZulu-Natal. Rare in South African waters.

ORIENTAL SWEETLIPS – *Plectorhinchus vittatus* (formerly *P. orientalis*)
Attains 86 cm. One of the most strikingly coloured sweetlips. Adults are whitish with longitudinal black stripes on sides extending to the belly. The black stripes are wider and darker on the upper body. Fins are yellow and the tail, anal and dorsal fins have large black spots. Juveniles are dark brown with several creamy blotches on the body and tail. Adults are encountered singly or in sizeable groups on outer coral reefs and in tropical lagoons. Juveniles frequent sheltered areas, remaining close to coral heads for protection and swim in an unusual undulating fashion. Ranges in depth from 2-40 m. Feeds mainly at night on bottom-living invertebrates. Ranges from Indo-Pacific south to central Mozambique. A common species.

GREY GRUNTER – *Pomadasys furcatum*
Attains 50 cm. A medium-sized, deep-bodied grunter with a steep head profile and a short snout. Overall body colour is silvery-grey with light and dark brown stripes running horizontally along the upper body. A shallow water shoaling fish, favouring sandy areas between scattered reefs in depths of 1-15 m. Feeds by blowing a jet of water down the holes of burrowing prawns and worms, forcing its prey out. Distribution is restricted to East Africa, Madagascar, extending south to KwaZulu-Natal. Rare south of Durban yet common off the northern KwaZulu-Natal coast.

JAVELIN GRUNTER – *Pomadasys kaakan*
Attains 50 cm. Juveniles have a long sloping forehead and a pointed snout. They are silvery with five dark broken bars on the sides and a dark patch on the gill cover. With growth, the markings disappear and adults become silvery overall, more robust and develop a distinctive bump on the forehead. Found in shallow coastal waters and estuaries in sandy or muddy areas, as well as on offshore banks down to 70 m. This bottom-feeder preys on shrimps and crabs, capturing them in the same manner as described for the grey grunter. Widespread throughout Indo-West Pacific, Red Sea, south to the Eastern Cape. Seldom seen by divers.

Harry hotlips

Barred rubberlips

Oriental sweetlips (adult)

Oriental sweetlips (juvenile)

Grey grunter

Javelin grunter

COCK GRUNTER – *Pomadasys multimaculatum*
Attains 60 cm. This oblong fish has a long sloping forehead and a pointed snout. Body colour is silvery, with a pale underside. Has numerous rows of dark brown spots on the upper sides, extending onto the head and snout. Frequents estuaries, lagoons and sandy shores and is often found swimming among shoals of spotted grunter. Captures crabs, worms and bivalve molluscs by blowing water into their muddy burrows to displace them. Widespread throughout Indo-West Pacific, Red Sea, south to the Eastern Cape. Not abundant in southern African waters. Very similar to the spotted grunter, *Pomadasys commersonnii*, which also has spots, but the spots do not extend on to the head.

Snappers – Family Lutjanidae

Snappers are a large family of medium-sized predatory fish, which inhabit shallow sub-tropical and tropical reefs, although the young sometimes live in estuaries. Many are strikingly patterned and coloured, varying greatly in shape. All have a single continuous dorsal fin and most have a shallow forked tail. Their common name is derived from their habit of snapping their jaws when hooked. They occur mostly in shoals, though some larger species may be solitary hunters and cave dwellers. Feeding habits vary according to species.

BLUE SMOOTHTOOTH JOBFISH (SMALL JOBFISH) – *Aphareus furca*
Attains 40 cm. This fish has an elongated body with a deeply forked tail. The back and upper sides are purplish brown and the lower sides steel-blue in colour. The mouth is large. The edges of the gill covers are distinctly dusky, as is the tail. Frequents the mid-water zone above or near offshore reefs, as well as tropical lagoons. Usually occurs singly, but may form small groups. Found in depths from 6-70 m. This roving snapper feeds on small fishes and crustaceans. Occurs throughout Indo-Pacific, Red Sea, south to northern KwaZulu-Natal. This curious and approachable species is relatively common.

GREEN JOBFISH (KAAKAP) – *Aprion virescens*
Attains 100 cm. A large slender fish with a blunt snout and a deeply forked tail. Its colour is usually dark green to bluish on the dorsal surface and pale below. Usually found singly in mid-water above reefs. A powerful predator, ranging from shallow to deep offshore reefs to a depth of 100 m. Diet consists mainly of fish and squid. Widespread throughout tropical Indo-Pacific, Red Sea, south to KwaZulu-Natal. A relatively common fish that always keeps its distance when approached underwater. Often caught by skiboat anglers and spearfishermen.

RIVER SNAPPER (MANGROVE SNAPPER) – *Lutjanus argentimaculatus*
Attains 100 cm. This large robust snapper has an elongated body with a long sloping forehead. Body colour is greenish brown to coppery red with a paler underside, and reddish fins. Its large mouth has prominent canines. Juveniles have distinctive white bands on the sides. Juveniles and sub-adults occur in estuaries, mangroves and rivers, whilst adults migrate to offshore reefs down to 80 m. Sometimes observed drifting in small groups close to the seabed, next to a reef. Preys on a variety of crustaceans and fishes. Ranges from Indo-West Pacific, Red Sea, south to the Eastern Cape. A relatively common species.

SPECKLED SNAPPER (SCRIBBLED SNAPPER) – *Lutjanus rivulatus*
Attains 60 cm. Deep, almost oval-shaped body and large lips. Colours are variable, but usually yellowish brown overall with light blue spots on each scale and thin, wavy blue lines on the head. The fins are yellow. Juveniles have a white spot on each side and a broad dark bar behind the head. Adults tend to remain close to ledges and in caves during the day. Occurs singly or in small groups, inhabiting inshore reef flats and offshore reefs down to at least 60 m. Preys on fishes, crabs, squid and octopus at night. Widespread throughout Indo-Pacific, Red Sea, south to central KwaZulu-Natal. An uncommon species.

EMPEROR SNAPPER – *Lutjanus sebae*
Attains 80 cm. This impressive snapper has a very deep body and a steep head profile. Adults pro-gressively become a deep red colour and the bands become fainter and may even disappear with age. Juveniles and sub-adults are silvery with three broad brown to reddish-brown bands on the sides of the body. Juveniles inhabit inshore reefs, estuaries and mangroves. This snapper inhabits coral and rocky reefs to a depth of at least 100 m. Diet consists of fishes and a variety of crustaceans. Widespread throughout Indo-West Pacific, Red Sea, south to central KwaZulu-Natal. An uncommon species.

Cock grunter

Blue smoothtooth jobfish

Green jobfish

River snapper

Speckled snapper

Emperor snapper

BLACK BEAUTY (BLACK SNAPPER) – *Macolor niger*

Attains 60 cm. The adults and juveniles are very different in appearance. Adults are robust and completely dark grey with black fins. Juveniles and sub-adults have black and white markings on body and fins. Adults often form groups along reef edges near deep water. Juveniles are solitary and swim about openly near the reef. Ranges in depth from 5-30 m. Feeds primarily on zooplankton at night. Occurs throughout tropical Indo-Pacific, Red Sea, south to KwaZulu-Natal. A relatively common species.

YELLOWTAIL FALSE FUSILIER (PROTEA BREAM OR YELLOWTAIL FUSILLIER) – *Paracaesio xanthura*

Attains 50 cm. Lower body and head are slate blue in colour. Upper body and tail are often yellow. Moves in shoals along and over offshore reefs. Generally occurs at depths greater than 20 m. Feeds almost exclusively on zooplankton. Widespread throughout Indo-West Pacific, Red Sea, extending to southern KwaZulu-Natal, where it is common. May be mistaken for a true fusilier (Caesio family).

FALSE FUSILIER SNAPPER (FUSILIER SNAPPER) – *Paracaesio sordidus*

Attains 50 cm. Distinguished by a deep, but streamlined, body profile and a large reddish-brown forked tail. Overall body colour is greenish grey, but paler on lower sides. Inhabits offshore reefs, especially along drop-offs. Encountered singly or in groups. It is reported to occur down to 100 m, but rises to the surface to feed on zooplankton. Widespread throughout Indo-Pacific, Red Sea, extending to KwaZulu-Natal. Relatively common, yet easily overlooked due to drab appearance. As with the yellowtail false fusilier, this snapper is often mistaken for a true fusilier.

Fusiliers – Family Caesionidae

Fusiliers are characterized by a slender streamlined body, a deeply forked tail and bright coloration. They are closely related to snappers and often occur in large shoals, swimming over and between reefs. The shoaling behaviour offers some protection against predatory fish, although fusiliers are often seen breaking the surface in an attempt to escape predators. Fusiliers generally occur in mid-water and are zooplankton feeders. They sometimes surround divers as they swim past.

LUNAR FUSILIER – *Caesio lunaris*

Attains 35 cm. Identified by its uniform blue colour and the distinctive black tips on the tail lobes. The tail and caudal peduncle of juveniles are yellow. Found in coastal areas mainly on or near coral reefs. Occurs in large shoals and often feeds further away from reefs than most other fusilier species. As with most fusiliers, it shelters in crevices on the reef at night. Ranges in depth from the surface to 40 m. Feeds on zooplankton. Widespread throughout Indo-Pacific, Red Sea, south to northern KwaZulu-Natal. A relatively common species.

YELLOW STRIPED FUSILIER – *Caesio* sp.

Attains 30 cm. The body is bluish dorsally, shading to a silvery pink below the lateral line. A distinctive horizontal yellow stripe, flanked by brown and blue lines, occurs along its side from head to tail. A dark margin marks each leading edge of the tail fin. Found in large shoals over and between reefs in depths ranging from the surface to 40 m. Feeds on zooplankton. Occurs off the east coast of southern Africa. Distribution in other regions is not readily known. A common species that was previously identified as the blue and gold fusilier, *Caesio caerulaureus*, but the colour pattern is distinctively different. There now seems to be doubt over correct identification.

Seabreams – Family Sparidae

Seabreams are an abundant family of fishes in southern African waters and are important linefish. They are characterized by their deep bodies and steep foreheads. Several species have been found to change sex. A large proportion of Sparid species are endemic to the southern African region. They are predominantly shoaling fishes, although some occur singly or in small groups. Feeding habits vary according to species.

SANTER (SOLDIER) – *Cheimerius nufar*

Attains 75 cm. Recognized by the oval-shaped body and silvery sheen, which is pinkish dorsally. Anal and pelvic fins have a bluish tinge. Juveniles and sub-adults have five faint red vertical crossbars on sides. Does not undergo sex change. Usually found singly or in loose groups on offshore reefs down to 80 m. Juveniles often occur in shallow protected waters. Feeds on fish and planktonic crustaceans. An Indo-Pacific species, extending to the south Western Cape. One of the most common and widespread of seabreams.

Black beauty (sub-adult)

Yellowtail false fusilier

False fusilier snapper

Lunar fusilier

Yellow striped fusilier

Santer

TWOBAR SEABREAM – *Acanthopagrus bifasciatus*

Attains 50 cm. Easily distinguished from other seabreams by the two vertical black crossbars on the head. Body is silvery with a yellowish hue on the dorsal surface. The tail, dorsal and pectoral fins are bright yellow. Has an oval body shape with a steep sloping forehead. Occurs singly or in loose groups and inhabits the sheltered waters of estuaries, bays and shallow coral reefs to a depth of 25 m. Feeds on hard-shelled bottom-dwelling invertebrates. Distribution ranges from the Red Sea, western Indian Ocean, to KwaZulu-Natal. Primarily a tropical species, occasionally found in northern KwaZulu-Natal.

SOLDIERBREAM – *Argyrops filamentosus*

Attains 60 cm. Deep body with steeply curved head profile and a bulge between the eyes. Third to seventh dorsal spines are distinctively long. Overall colour is silvery-pink with an iridescent silvery-bluish sheen. Juveniles sometimes have faint crossbars. Usually occurs in shoals on the flat outer fringes of offshore reefs and sometimes around pinnacles. Ranges in depth from 20-50 m. Feeds on crabs, molluscs and hard-shelled invertebrates, which are crushed with its powerful jaws. Widespread throughout the Red Sea, western Indian Ocean, south to central KwaZulu-Natal. Uncommon and rarely seen by divers. Frequently confused with the king soldier bream, *Argyrops spinifer*, which is distinguished by its shorter dorsal spines.

CARPENTER (SILVERFISH) – *Argyrozona argyrozona*

Attains 90 cm but 60 cm is more common. Moderately elongated silvery-pink body with narrow pale blue dotted stripes along the sides. The forehead is reddish and the fins are pinkish to translucent. An offshore fish, ranging in depth from 20-200 m. Preys on crabs, anchovies, squid and worms. This species is endemic to the eastern and south western Cape coasts. Spawning takes place mainly on the Agulhas Bank during spring and summer. A common and important commercial linefish in the Cape.

FRANSMADAM (KAREL GROOTOOG) – *Boopsoidea inornata*

Attains 35 cm. One of the smaller members of the seabream family. It has a fairly deep body with a pointed snout, small mouth, large eyes and a prominent lateral line. Body colour is brown to silvery with a distinct bronze sheen. A dark bar marks the edge of the gill cover. Juveniles are silvery with orange fins. Can occur singly or in small groups. Found over rocky reefs ranging in depth from 5-40 m. An omnivore that feeds on red bait, molluscs, worms and a variety of seaweeds. This endemic species is known from the southern Western Cape to southern KwaZulu-Natal. A common fish, regarded as a pest by anglers as it nibbles the bait intended for larger fish.

DAGERAAD – *Chrysoblephus cristiceps*

Attains 70 cm but 40 cm is more common. Readily identified by the coppery body colour with iridescent shades of gold and reddish pink. Short blue lines occur above and below each eye. A black spot marks the end of the dorsal fin. The body shape is noticeably deep with a pointed snout and a steep sloping forehead, concave below the eyes. This fish has the ability to change sex. A shoaling species, found over rocky reefs to depths of between 20-100 m. Diet consists of small fish and bottom-living invertebrates. Known only from False Bay in the Western Cape to southern KwaZulu-Natal. An important linefish species that is relatively common.

RED STUMPNOSE – *Chrysoblephus gibbiceps*

Attains 60 cm. This deep-bodied robust fish has a very steep forehead, which is slightly concave below the eyes, and a deeply forked tail. Adult males develop a large hump on the forehead. The background colour is silvery-pink with five to seven red vertical bands with numerous irregular black spots over the body. Occurs singly or in small groups on offshore reefs to depths of 150 m. Preys on crabs, molluscs and urchins, which are crushed by its powerful jaws. An endemic species, found only between False Bay in the Western Cape and East London. A relatively common seabream, which is more abundant during summer.

Twobar seabream

Soldierbream

Carpenter

Fransmadam

Dageraad

Red stumpnose

ROMAN – *Chrysoblephus laticeps*

Attains 50 cm. This fish is not as deep-bodied as other *Chrysoblephus* species and the forehead is less steep. The body colour is distinctively brownish orange to scarlet red. Prominent white saddle on the back. Also has a white bar marking the gill cover, and a blue line between the eyes. The canine teeth are large and conspicuous. This seabream undergoes sex change from female to male at a size of about 30 cm. Occurs singly or in small groups, frequenting inshore and offshore reefs to depths of 100 m. Feeds on a variety of shellfish, urchins and worms. This common cool-water species is endemic to South Africa and is found between Cape Town and the Eastern Cape.

FALSE ENGLISHMAN – *Chrysoblephus lophus*

Attains 50 cm. This species has noticeably elongated dorsal fin spines and a grooved forehead. Other features include a deep body, a steep sloping forehead and a deeply forked tail fin. Coloration is silvery-pink with six to seven red crossbars. Favours deeper offshore reefs down to 150 m. Preys on shellfish, urchins, crabs and occasionally small fish. Blows a jet of water in to the sand to expose prey. Known from KwaZulu-Natal to southern Mozambique, but may range more widely in the Indian Ocean. Not an abundant species. Similar colour pattern to the Englishman, *Chrysoblephus anglicus,* which lacks grooves on the forehead, and does not have extended dorsal fin spines.

BLACK MUSSELCRACKER (POENSKOP) – *Cymatoceps nasutus*

Attains 120 cm. One of the largest members of the seabream family. It has a robust body and a rounded head profile. The body shape varies with age. Adults are sooty-grey to black in colour and develop a large white fleshy 'nose'. Sub-adults are of a lighter grey with two dark vertical crossbars on sides. Juveniles are very different, being greenish brown with several white blotches or white lines on the body. This solitary species is found on inshore and offshore rocky reefs at depths of 5-60 m. Juveniles frequent shallow weedy areas. A powerful predator of crabs, crayfish, sea urchins and molluscs. Prey is crushed by the grinding movement of the strong jaws and molars. An endemic species, ranging from the Western Cape to southern Mozambique. More abundant in winter along the East Coast. Much prized by shore and ski-boat fishermen. An extremely slow growing species, reaching ages in excess of 40 years. Heavily over-exploited.

JANBRUIN (JOHN BROWN) – *Gymnocrotaphus curvidens*

Attains 50 cm. This robust, plump-bodied fish has a steep forehead and a protruding mouth. A slight bump develops over the eyes with age. Overall colour is dark brown, with a blue eye ring. Has large yellow protruding front teeth. Found on rocky reefs to a depth of 30 m. Usually solitary, feeding mainly on red-bait, which it tears off with its strong teeth. Seaweed and small crustaceans are also eaten. Limited distribution, occurring only between the southern Western Cape and Eastern Cape. Relatively common. Often taken by spearfishermen, as it is easily approached underwater.

WHITE STEENBRAS (PIGNOSE GRUNTER) – *Lithognathus lithognathus*

Attains 100 cm. This species has an elongated body with a long sloping forehead and pointed snout. Body colour is silvery grey with dark vertical crossbars on the sides, which tend to fade with age. Juveniles live mainly in estuaries and lagoons, while adults inhabit shallow sandy bays. Sometimes enters estuaries to feed as it is able to tolerate low salinity levels. Occurs singly or in small groups and ranges in depth from 1-20 m. Prey is captured by using its long pointed snout to blow a jet of water into sandy burrows to displace shrimps and mud-prawns. Crabs and molluscs are also eaten. Endemic to South Africa, extending from the Western Cape to southern KwaZulu-Natal. During the winter breeding season, large shoals of adult fish migrate up the east coast as far as the central Eastern Cape. A common and much-prized angling fish.

Roman

False Englishman

Black musselcracker

Black musselcracker (juvenile)

Janbruin

White steenbras

SAND STEENBRAS – *Lithognathus mormyrus*
Attains 30 cm. A small seabream with an elongated body and a rather long pointed snout. Overall colour is silver, with approximately 14 narrow brown crossbars on the sides. Fins are translucent to dusky. As the name suggests, it is a sand-dwelling species, using its colour pattern to blend with the sand ripples on the seabed. Ranges in depth from 1-40 m. Occurs singly or in small groups. Forages for shrimps, molecrabs and bivalve molluscs living in the sand. Occurs around most of the African coast and in the Mediterranean Sea. Particularly abundant in sandy bays along the Western Cape coast. A generally common species.

BLUE HOTTENTOT – *Pachymetopon aeneum*
Attains 60 cm. Slightly elongate body, especially towards the caudal peduncle. The colour varies from blue to silvery-bronze, with a bluish head. Occurs singly or in groups, frequenting rocky offshore reefs in depths of 15-80 m. Feeds on encrusted organisms such as ascidians and sponges, and to a lesser extent seaweed. Known only from the Western Cape to northern KwaZulu-Natal. A common species that is an important fish in the commercial line-fishery. May be confused with the hottentot *Pachymetopon blochii* from the West Coast, which has a plumper body and an overall bluish-grey colour with a dorsal golden-green sheen. Also similar to the German *Polyamblyodon germanum*, which has a steeper forehead and a silvery-grey colour.

BRONZE BREAM – *Pachymetopon grande*
Attains 65 cm. Largest of the *Pachymetopon* genus. This seabream is noticeably plump and oval shaped, with a small head and a bump over the eyes. The overall colour is bronze. The side of the head is often iridescent blue. Normally a solitary species that occurs along shallow, turbulent, rocky shores, but occasionally seen on deeper offshore reefs. Ranges in depth between 2-30 m. Feeds on seaweeds and invertebrates. Ranges from the Western Cape, extending up the East Coast of Africa and across to Madagascar. More common during late winter and spring. This fish is commonly caught by shore anglers and spearfishermen. Similar to the German *Polyamblyodon germanum*, which has an overall silvery grey colour.

SAND SOLDIER (RED TJOR TJOR) – *Pagellus bellottii natalensis*
Attains 35 cm. This small, active seabream is pinkish dorsally and silvery-white ventrally with numerous horizontal rows of iridescent blue spots along the sides of body. Has reddish fins and a red spot on the upper gill cover. Lives in groups, primarily over sandy bottoms away from reefs at depths exceeding 20 m. Diet consists of bottom-living invertebrates and small fishes. Ranges from Eastern Cape, up the East coast of Africa and across to Madagascar. Particularly abundant off the KwaZulu-Natal coast. Its coloration makes it inconspicuous in a sandy, open water habitat.

RED STEENBRAS (COPPER STEENBRAS) – *Petrus rupestris*
Attains 200 cm but 130 cm is more common. The largest member of the seabream family. Has a robust, elongated reddish-brown body with a yellow underside. Adults move into deeper water with age, and males develop a yellow colour with black markings on the head and back. This powerful predator occurs near rocky reefs to depths of 160 m, feeding on smaller fish, octopus and squid. A southern African endemic, ranging from the Western Cape to central KwaZulu-Natal. It is a particularly active and aggressive species, that was once abundant but has been drastically reduced in numbers over the years due to over-exploitation.

CRISTIE – *Polyamblyodon gibbosum*
Attains 50 cm. Robust, moderately deep body with a steep sloping forehead and a slightly protruding snout. Bluish grey overall with dusky to pale yellow fins. Can be distinguished from similar species by its strongly defined lateral line and by the long pectoral fins. Ranges in depth from 2-25 m. Forms loose shoals above reefs, where it feeds on drifting zooplankton. Known only from KwaZulu-Natal to central Mozambique and Madagascar. Particularly common on the Alliwal Shoal and Sodwana Bay reefs. An inquisitive fish, which often approaches divers during their ascent to the surface. May be confused with the blue hottentot, *Pachymetopon aeneum,* and the German *Polyamblyodon germanum*.

Sand steenbras

Blue hottentot

Bronze bream

Sand soldier

Red steenbras

Cristie

SCOTSMAN – *Polysteganus praeorbitalis*
Attains 90 cm. The body shape is very distinctive, making identification easy. This fish has a very steep forehead, a deep body tapering towards the tail and small eyes. The body colour is pinkish with numerous blue dots on the upper body, and blue lines around the eyes. The underside of the snout is also bluish. A solitary species, inhabiting offshore reefs at depths of between 20-100 m. This powerful predator preys on crustaceans, fish and squid. An uncommon seabream, known only from Eastern Cape to Beira in Mozambique. The numbers of this fish have diminished greatly due to fishing pressure.

SEVENTY-FOUR – *Polysteganus undulosus*
Attains 100 cm. This colourful seabream has a moderately elongated body with a smoothly curved upper profile and a slightly convex head. The overall colour is pinkish or greenish dorsally and paler ventrally, with four to six horizontal iridescent blue stripes along the sides. Has a conspicuous black mark across the lateral line just behind the pectoral fin. Predominately shoaling, especially during late winter when spawning takes place. Associated with deeper reefs and pinnacles to depths of 200 m. Feeds on small fish, squid and larger zooplankton. An endemic species, ranging from the southern Eastern Cape to southern Mozambique. Although this species was once abundant, stocks have collapsed due to over-fishing. A moratorium now exists on possession of this species. Rarely seen by divers.

DANE – *Porcostoma dentata*
Attains 30 cm. Attractive, small, plump-bodied seabream with a distinctive orange-red colour and pale underside. A red blotch decorates the base of the pectoral fin, and a purple line joins the eyes. Occurs singly or in small groups on offshore reefs in depths of 25-100 m. Uses its strong teeth for crushing a variety of hard-shelled invertebrates, such as crabs and mantis shrimps. Known only from southern KwaZulu-Natal to Beira in Mozambique and fairly common on reefs off southern KwaZulu-Natal.

WHITE STUMPNOSE – *Rhabdosargus globiceps*
Attains 50 cm. Has a blunt snout, deep body, and a steep forehead. Body is silvery with six to seven dark vertical crossbars on the sides. Juveniles use estuaries as nursery areas. Often forms large shoals over sandy bottoms, usually near reefs or rocky outcrops, to depths of 80 m. Adults are carnivorous, feeding on crabs, bivalve molluscs and other crustaceans, whilst juveniles are omnivorous. Occurs only from Angola to Eastern Cape. Common. An economically important fish caught by line and seine-net fishermen in the Cape.

STEENTJIE – *Spondyliosoma emarginatum*
Attains 45 cm but 30 cm is more common. Moderately elongated body with a pointed head. Colour is variable. It can be olive-green dorsally and silvery-blue on lower sides with a prominent yellow mid-lateral stripe and flanked by thin blue and yellow lines, or blue-grey with a pale underside and several pale yellow stripes on upper sides. This species exhibits unusual courtship display and develops a strong breeding pattern associated with pre-spawning: males construct a nest by creating a shallow depression in the sand next to the reef, which they guard until the eggs are hatched. Often occurs in sizeable shoals over rocky reefs, in depths of 5-30 m. Diet consists of a variety of small crustaceans and worms and sometimes grazes on algae. An endemic species, known only from the Western Cape to KwaZulu-Natal. Often preyed upon by larger predatory fish. A common species.

Emperors – Family Lethrinidae
Emperors are medium to large snapper-like fish. Most have elongate bodies, pointed heads and relatively thick fleshy lips. They generally lack bright colours. Most species of the genus *Lethrinus* are able to rapidly adopt a dark mottled or reticular colour pattern, which can be 'turned' on or off depending on its mood. They are shoaling and solitary fishes confined to warmer waters, and are usually found on the sandy fringes of coral and rocky reefs, where they forage in the sand for prey.

BLACKSPOT EMPEROR (BLACKPATCH EMPEROR) – *Lethrinus harak*
Attains 60 cm but 40 cm is more common. The body is elongated with a pronounced snout. Recognized by its overall whitish colour and prominent black patch ringed in yellow on the side of body. This patch may be indistinct in some individuals. The body is elongate with a pronounced snout. Generally solitary, but occasionally occurs in small groups. Inhabits shallow water and is found over sand and rubble areas, reef flats or seagrass beds. Ranges in depth from 1-20 m. Preys on a variety of bottom-living invertebrates and small fishes. Widespread throughout Indo-West Pacific, Red Sea, south to northern KwaZulu-Natal. A relatively common species.

Scotsman

Seventy-four

Dane

White stumpnose

Steentjie

Blackspot emperor

GREY BARENOSE – *Gymnocranius griseus*

Attains 80 cm. One of the larger members of the emperor family. However, much smaller individuals are usually encountered. This species has a slightly elongated body with a pointed snout and large eyes. The body colour is silvery-grey with a vertical black bar through the eye. Large adults develop blue lines on the cheek. Juveniles have several faint dark bars on the sides, which tend to fade with age. Favours tropical waters, where it inhabits sandy areas adjacent to inshore and offshore reefs in depths of 5-80 m. Tends to swim well above the bottom, searching for prey such as crustaceans and small fish. Widespread throughout Indo-West Pacific, south to KwaZulu-Natal. A relatively common species.

BIGEYE BARENOSE – *Monotaxis grandoculis*

Attains 60 cm but 40 cm is more common. Juveniles are whitish with black upper sides and have three distinct vertical white bars on the upper body. They also have a vertical black bar across the large eyes. With age, the head becomes heavier and the snout more blunt. The black colour fades and turns uniform silvery-grey. A yellow vertical bar also develops on the gill cover. Normally found over sandy bottoms, near channels and reef fringes. Occurs in depths ranging from 5-60 m. Adults congregate over reefs during the day, dispersing at night to feed on a variety of bottom-living creatures in deep water. Small juveniles are solitary and inhabit rubble and sandy areas. Occurs throughout Indo-Pacific, Red Sea, south to KwaZulu-Natal. A relatively common species.

Spinecheeks (Butterfly breams) – Family Nemipteridae

Spinecheeks are a large family of fish, closely related to the snappers. They comprise small to medium-sized fish that have a moderately elongated body with large scales, a small mouth and a single dorsal fin. Members of the genus *Scolopsis* have a backward pointing spine located below the eye, hence the common family name. Spinecheeks are usually brightly coloured, elegant fish, which are most abundant amongst inshore coral heads. They typically swim close to the bottom for a short distance, stopping suddenly to search the seabed for possible prey. They constitute an important food source in some areas.

SILVERFLASH SPINECHEEK (ARABIAN SPINECHEEK) – *Scolopsis ghanam*

Attains 20 cm. Distinctive silvery-grey colour with numerous black or dark brown spots on sides, and alternating white and dark brown stripes above the lateral line extending onto the head. Fins are bluish grey. Occurs singly or in pairs and frequents shallow inshore areas near coral reefs. Ranges in depth from 1-20 m. Feeds on worms and small bottom-living invertebrates. Found throughout western Indian Ocean, Red Sea, Arabian Sea, extending to southern Mozambique. Generally common but rare in South African waters.

PALEBAND SPINECHEEK (WHITECHEEK MONOCLE BREAM) – *Scolopsis vosmeri*

Attains 25 cm. This species has a smoothly curved body profile and a pointed snout. The body colour is variable but most individuals are reddish brown with a pale underside and a prominent broad white bar extending across the head and gill covers. Fins are yellow or orange. Inhabits inshore sheltered coral and rocky reefs, shipwrecks and lagoons, in depths ranging from 5-45 m. Also found occasionally in rivermouths. Occurs singly or in pairs and preys on bottom-living invertebrates and worms. Widespread throughout tropical Indo-West Pacific, Red Sea, south to central KwaZulu-Natal. A relatively common species in most areas, but uncommon in South African waters.

Galjoens – Family Coracinidae

This family comprises two species, the banded galjoen, *Coracinus multifasciatus,* and the galjoen *Dichistius capensis*. They have plump bodies with fine scales and small mouths. Galjoens are confined to coastal waters and are found along rocky shores and on shallow reefs.

GALJOEN (DAMBA) – *Dichistius capensis*

Attains 80 cm. This galjoen is recognized by its deep robust body, which varies in colour from uniform grey to black. Confined to the turbulent surf-zone, where it is found in small groups, feeding on a wide range of plant and animal material. This endemic species is South Africa's national fish and ranges from Angola to southern KwaZulu-Natal. It prefers cooler waters and is an important shore-angling fish along the eastern and western Cape coast.

Grey barenose

Bigeye barenose

Bigeye barenose (juvenile)

Silverflash spinecheek

Paleband spinecheek

Galjoen

Jutjaw fish – Family Parascorpididae

Parascorpis typus

Attains 60 cm. The jutjaw family comprises a single species. The body is deep and oval with a long, sloping concave forehead and a forked tail. The large mouth has a projecting lower jaw. Adults are dull silvery-grey to brown, while juveniles have several distinct, cream coloured longitudinal stripes on the sides. Adults frequent deeper offshore reefs to depths of 40 m but also occur in kelp beds along the southern Western Cape coast. Juveniles inhabit rocky shores and shallow reefs, where they shelter near overhangs or in caves. Feeds on zooplankton, shrimps and small fishes. Known only from False Bay in the Western Cape to southern Mozambique. Fairly common in cooler waters.

Chubs (rudderfish) – Family Kyphosidae

Chubs lack distinctive markings. They are plump, robust fish with small heads. They are more common in shallow, turbulent waters, but also occur on offshore reefs. They have the ability to abruptly adopt a pattern of pale blotches evenly spaced over the body and head, depending on their mood. Their diet consists exclusively of seaweed.

BRASSY CHUB (LOWFIN RUDDERFISH) – *Kyphosus vaigiensis*

Attains 60 cm. Overall slate-blue colour with narrow longitudinal bronze lines on sides and two short bronze lines below the eye. The photograph shows a typical blotched pattern. Frequents inshore and offshore reefs. Rarely occurs deeper than 15 m. Sometimes congregates in sizeable numbers to feed on seaweed. Widespread throughout Indo-Pacific, south to the Eastern Cape. An uncommon species.

Batfishes – Family Ephippidae

The batfish family is characterized by a deep, highly compressed, almost circular body with a short head and small mouth. Juveniles have extremely long dorsal and anal fins, which become less exaggerated with growth. Adults can be solitary or form small groups, often in mid-water above a reef. Batfish swim with a distinctive, slow, waggling motion and are often curious towards divers.

LONGFIN BATFISH – *Platax teira*

Attains 50 cm. The body colour is light brown with three darker brown crossbars, one of which traverses the eye. The crossbars tend to fade with age. The main diagnostic features are the black blotch below the pectoral fin and the short dark bar on the anus. Usually found in groups on reefs, shipwrecks and around jetties at depths of 1-30 m. Feeds on algae and small invertebrates. Widespread throughout Indo-West Pacific, the Red Sea, south to the Eastern Cape. Common and similar to the orbicular batfish, *Platax orbicularis*, which only has a single black bar just above the pelvic fin.

Pursemouths – Family Gerreidae

Small to medium-sized silvery fishes with deeply forked tails, which occur in warm seas and sometimes in brackish water. They are bottom-feeders, using their extendable mouth as a tube. They occur singly or in small loose groups. They tend to swim slowly over sandy bottoms, stopping suddenly to search for food.

SMALLSCALE PURSEMOUTH (POUTER OR SILVER BIDDIES) – *Gerres longirostris*

Attains 25 cm. Elongated body with a pointed snout, long sloping forehead and deeply forked tail. Body colour is silvery-grey, with dusky spots along sides forming faint vertical bars. Inside edge of the tail fin is often dark blue. A solitary species inhabiting shallow coastal waters and estuaries in depths of 1-20 m near sandy and rubble areas. Feeds on small bottom-dwelling invertebrates. Widespread throughout Indo-Pacific, south to the Eastern Cape. A common species, previously known as *Gerres acinaces*.

Goatfishes – Family Mullidae

Goatfishes have a slender body, a deeply forked tail and whisker-like barbels. They are usually found over sandy areas near reefs, busily probing the sand for prey. May be followed by a lone kingfish, hoping to prey on creatures disturbed from the seabed. Some species are solitary, whilst others form shoals.

GOLDSADDLE GOATFISH (YELLOWSADDLE GOATFISH) – *Parupeneus cyclostomus*

Attains 50 cm. Unusual in that it has two distinct colour variations. One is yellowish grey with blue markings on scales resulting in an overall blue hue, and a prominent yellow saddle-like spot on upper caudal peduncle. The other is entirely yellow. Both variations have blue streaks on the head. Found on coral reefs and adjacent rubble bottoms in depths of 5-100 m. Unlike other goatfishes, its diet consists mainly of small reef fishes. Common throughout Indo-West Pacific, Red Sea, south to KwaZulu-Natal.

Jutjaw

Brassy chub

Longfin batfish

Smallscale pursemouth

Goldsaddle goatfish (blue form)

Goldsaddle goatfish (yellow form)

BLACKSPOT GOATFISH (SIDESPOT GOATFISH) – *Parupeneus pleurostigma*
Attains 30 cm. This species has a prominent black blotch on its side with a white area to the rear of the blotch. Body colour is pinkish dorsally and white on the lower sides and the belly. Blue streaks are present on the head. Found in shallow sandy or rubble areas of coral reefs in depths ranging from 10-40 m. Usually encountered singly or in small groups. Feeds on a variety of bottom-living invertebrates and fishes. A reasonably common species throughout Indo-West Pacific, Red Sea, south to KwaZulu-Natal.

YELLOWSTRIPE GOATFISH – *Mulloidichthys flavolineatus*
Attains 40 cm. This fish has a mid-lateral yellow stripe. A small black blotch is present below the first dorsal fin. Body colour is grey to olive dorsally and whitish on the sides and belly. Black blotch can be 'turned off' according to mood. Found in sandy bays and offshore reefs to depths of 50 m. Occurs singly or in large shoals. Feeds on bottom-dwelling crustaceans. Widespread throughout Indo-Pacific, the Red Sea, south to the Eastern Cape. Relatively common. Similar to the yellowfin goatfish *M. vanicolensis* when blotch is turned off.

Kobs – Family Sciaenidae
A large family that has a worldwide distribution. They frequent marine, brackish and fresh waters and are generally silvery or dull coloured, with a robust, elongated body. Most have a conspicuous lateral line and a truncate tail fin. These large predators often form shoals. They inhabit estuaries, shallow shores and deeper offshore reefs. Some species are bottom-dwelling and have adapted to the murky conditions.

GEELBEK (CAPE SALMON) – *Atractoscion aequidens*
Attains 120 cm. A slender, robust body with a concave tail fin. The upper half of the head and body is brown and the underside is pale silvery. A short brown line occurs along the upper lip. The interior of the mouth and gill cover is bright yellow. Inhabits offshore reefs to depths of 100 m. A powerful predator, feeding on fish such as sardines and anchovies. Ranges from Angola to KwaZulu-Natal and also found off southeastern Australia. In winter, shoals of these fish migrate from the southern Western Cape to KwaZulu-Natal to spawn. Rarely seen by divers. Heavily over-exploited by recreational and commercial fishing.

BAARDMAN (TASSELFISH OR BELLMAN) – *Umbrina canariensis*
Attains 55 cm. Has a deep body and a steep head profile, with short thick barbels under the lower jaw. Body colour is uniform grey-brown. A sluggish fish that congregates in small shoals, sometimes with other fish species. Also occurs singly. Usually found over sandy areas near reefs at depths of 10-40 m. Preys on small bottom-dwelling invertebrates. Distribution includes the Red Sea and the west, south and east coasts of Africa. Commonly found in Eastern and Western Cape waters.

Angelfishes – Family Pomacanthidae
Angelfishes are considered to be among the most beautiful and majestic of all reef fishes. These small to medium-sized, laterally compressed and oval-shaped fishes are similar in habit and shape to butterflyfishes. However, a prominent, backward-projecting spine extending from part of the lower gill cover distinguishes them from butterflyfishes. They have very striking colour patterns, and the juveniles of some species differ significantly in colour pattern from the adults. They are mostly solitary, but in some species occur in small groups.

YELLOWBAR ANGELFISH (ARABIAN ANGELFISH) – *Pomacanthus maculosus*
Attains 50 cm. This angelfish has a prominent vertical yellow blotch on its side, which extends for most of the body depth. Overall colour is blue or brownish purple with scattered black spots on upper head and body. The soft dorsal and anal fins have extended rays. Juveniles are strikingly different in coloration, and have alternating blue and white, slightly curved, vertical lines on a dark blue to black background. Generally solitary, but occasionally encountered in pairs. Frequents shallow coral reefs. Ranges in depth from 4-15 m. Diet comprises primarily sponges, invertebrates and algae. Ranges from the Red Sea, Arabian Sea, East Africa, south to central Mozambique. A relatively common species.

GOLDTAIL ANGELFISH (AFRICAN ANGELFISH) – *Pomacanthus chrysurus*
Attains 33 cm. Distinguished by a bright yellow tail and a black body, with alternating wide and narrow vertical white lines, curved backwards. Irregular blue markings are present on the head and snout. Juveniles have a similar colour pattern to adults, but the white lines are more pronounced. A solitary species that inhabits shallow reefs in depths of 1-25 m. Known to crossbreed with the yellowbar angelfish, *Pomacanthus maculosus*. Feeds mainly on invertebrates. Found off the East African coast from the Gulf of Aden to Mozambique, and eastwards to the Seychelles. An uncommon species.

Blackspot goatfish

Yellowstripe goatfish

Geelbek

Baardman

Yellowbar angelfish

Goldtail angelfish

SWALLOWTAIL ANGELFISH (LYRETAIL OR ZEBRA ANGELFISH) – *Genicanthus caudovittatus*
Attains 20 cm. It has a more elongated body compared to most other members of the angelfish family and a distinctive lunate tail with elongated lobes. Head profile is blunt and rounded. Males are pale bluish, with a black-barred pattern on the side of body and upper head. Females are whitish grey overall, but darker dorsally with a broad black margin on each caudal fin lobe and a black bar above the eye. Frequents moderately deep rocky and coral offshore reefs. Usually encountered in small groups comprising one male and several females, swimming a few metres above the reef. Ranges in depth from between 25-70 m. Feeds primarily on zooplankton. Ranges throughout the western Indian Ocean, Red Sea and extends to particular locations off southern KwaZulu-Natal. Rare in south African waters.

Butterflyfishes – Family Chaetodontidae
Butterflyfishes are small to medium-sized, laterally compressed fishes with a disc-shaped profile. Their size and slightly concave forehead make them distinguishable from the larger similar shaped angelfishes, which have rounded foreheads. Their eyes are generally concealed by dark bars on the head. These, and the false eye-spots found near the tail on several species, are markings to confuse predators.

COACHMAN (THREADBACK OR LONGFIN BANNERFISH) – *Heniochus acuminatus*
Attains 25 cm. This unusually shaped butterflyfish has a long white dorsal filament, two broad black oblique bands on a white body, and a soft yellow dorsal tail and pectoral fins. A distinctive black mark occurs above and between the eyes. Occurs singly or in small groups and is usually seen swimming close to a reef. Inhabits coral and rocky reefs and sheltered harbour areas at depths of 1-40 m. Juveniles sometimes remove parasites from other fish for food. Feeds on zooplankton, bottom-living invertebrates and algae. Widespread throughout Indo-West Pacific, the Red Sea, south to the Eastern Cape. A common species that is very similar to the schooling coachman, *Heniochus diphreutes*, but has a longer snout and a more rounded anal fin tip.

SCHOOLING COACHMAN (SCHOOLING BANNERFISH) – *Heniochus diphreutes*
Attains 16 cm. This species has a similar colour pattern to the coachman. It is distinguished by its slightly smaller size, shorter snout and a more rounded body profile. Also, the second black band ends very close to the tip of the anal fin, which is more angular in shape. The blackish marking above and between the eyes extends higher up the forehead and is less distinct than on the coachman. Juveniles usually remain close to the reef, and sometimes feed on parasites, which they remove from other fish. Ranges in depth from 5-200 m, but generally below 15 m. Adults typically form very large shoals of up to several hundred that swim over and between reefs, feeding on zooplankton. Occurs throughout Indo-West Pacific to Hawaii, extending to southern KwaZulu-Natal.

Kingfishes (jacks or trevallies) – Family Carangidae
The family comprises 140 species worldwide with at least 50 members occurring off the southern African east coast, including pompanos, scads, queenfishes, yellowtails, garricks, rainbow runners and maasbankers. They vary considerably in body shape, size and colour. Most are strongly compressed silvery and streamlined fishes with a narrow caudal peduncle usually reinforced by a series of bony scutes, and a deeply forked tail. Juveniles generally have barred markings. Kingfishes are strong swimming pelagic predators. Various species may regularly visit reefs, singly or in groups, in search of food. They are amongst the most active predators on the reef, the smaller species feeding on zooplankton and the larger ones taking smaller fishes. In the open sea, they usually hunt in groups for shoaling fish such as sardines and anchovies. Juveniles may seek refuge under floating objects. Many of the family are popular food and sport fishes throughout the world.

THREADFIN MIRRORFISH (PENNANT TREVALLY) – *Alectis ciliaris*
Attains 100 cm. A deep bodied and extremely compressed fish. Its body shape changes considerably with growth, but always retains a rounded head profile. Adults are silvery overall with a bluish hue dorsally and pale to pearly ventrally. Juveniles are more diamond-shaped in profile and have very long dorsal and anal fin rays, resembling streamers. They also have several dusky crossbars on the sides and pale yellow to dusky fins. The pelagic juveniles mimic jellyfish as a defense mechanism. Adults are solitary and inhabit coastal waters to a depth of 100 m. Feeds mainly on bottom-living crustaceans and small fish. Distribution ranges from the Eastern Cape, northwards to the Red Sea, India and eastern Australia. Uncommon and rarely seen by divers. Adults are often confused with the Indian mirrorfish, *Alectis indicus,* which has a much steeper, slightly concave forehead.

Swallowtail angelfish (male)

Swallowtail angelfish (female)

Coachman

Schooling coachman

Threadfin mirrorfish

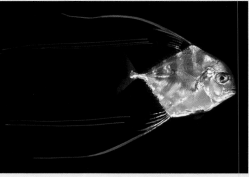

Threadfin mirrorfish (juvenile)

SHRIMP SCAD – *Alepes djedaba*

Attains 34 cm. A small kingfish recognized by its yellowish tail and by the black blotch on the upper edge of the gill cover. The overall colour is silvery, but greyish green when viewed from above, and whitish below. The body profile is smoothly curved. This active predator is often encountered in large shoals near inshore and shallow offshore reefs. Often gathers around rocky pinnacles and shipwrecks. Ranges in depth from 2-50 m and feeds on a variety of free-swimming crustaceans. Occurs in the Red Sea and throughout Indo-West Pacific, extending to KwaZulu-Natal. A relatively common species.

COASTAL KINGFISH (SHORTFIN KINGFISH OR BLUE SPINED TREVALLY) – *Carangoides caeruleopinnatus*

Attains 40 cm. A deep bodied species almost oval in shape with a steep forehead. Overall colour is silvery, but bluish green from above. Irregular pale yellow spots occur on the upper sides. Fins are yellow-green or dusky. Juveniles are strongly banded, and usually solitary, while adults occur in pairs or small groups. Inhabits coastal reefs and tropical lagoons to a depth of 40 m. Feeds on crustaceans and small fish. Widespread throughout Indo-West Pacific, south to central KwaZulu-Natal. A common kingfish.

YELLOWSPOTTED KINGFISH (YELLOW-DOTTED TREVALLY) – *Carangoides fulvoguttatus*

Attains 100 cm. Has an elongated body with a rounded snout. Overall colour is silvery with a greenish dorsal surface. Usually has many small yellow spots on upper sides arranged in four vertical bands. Large adults often have three black blotches on mid-lateral line and numerous black dots on chest. Occurs in small groups that patrol the edges of coastal reefs and occasionally offshore banks to a depth of 100 m. Feeds on invertebrates and small fish. Widespread throughout Indo-West Pacific, Red Sea, extending to southern KwaZulu-Natal. A relatively common species, very similar to the bludger, *Caraneoides gymno-stethus*, but distinguished from it by higher-set eyes and banded arrangement of the yellow spots.

GIANT KINGFISH (GIANT TREVALLY) – *Caranx ignobilis*

Attains 160 cm. The giant kingfish is the king of all kingfishes. It is readily identified by its deep robust body, steep forehead and long sickle-shaped pectoral fins. Adults are generally silvery-grey with a darker dorsal surface and a pale underside. Small black spots are scattered on its sides and the fins are greyish to black. An extremely fierce predator that hunts day and night. Adults occur singly or in small groups. They are mostly found along the outer edges of reefs and around offshore pinnacles ranging in depths from 1-50 m. Diet consists primarily of fish, but squid, mantis shrimps and other crustaceans are also eaten. Widespread and common throughout Indo-West Pacific, south to the Eastern Cape. The giant kingfish is much prized by spearfishermen and sports anglers.

RAINBOW RUNNER – *Elagatis bipinnulata*

Attains 120 cm but 80 cm is more common. This swift and graceful predator has a slender streamlined body with a pointed head and a large forked tail. A striking fish, easily recognized by the distinctive double light blue lines along the sides, separated by a broader olive or green stripe. General body colour is dark olive green dorsally and silvery-white ventrally. A pelagic species, usually found in small groups in mid-water over reefs. Ranges in depth from 1-50 m. Feeds on small fish, squid and swimming crustaceans, such as crab larvae and krill. Occurs in all tropical seas, extending to southern KwaZulu-Natal. This relatively common fish is an important food source for larger billfish. Often makes a close pass to divers, probably attracted by their bubbles.

GOLDEN KINGFISH (GOLDEN TREVALLY) – *Gnathanodon speciosus*

Attains 110 cm. Juveniles and sub-adults have a striking yellow colour with a black barred pattern, and yellow fins. With age the yellow becomes more silvery and the barring fades and several black spots appear on the sides. Often hunts in small groups. Juveniles mimic true pilotfish behaviour with sharks and other large fishes such as groupers and rays. Frequents coastal coral and rocky reefs to a depth of 50 m. A bottom-feeder that uses its highly protractible mouth to suck up food items such as shrimps, crabs, molluscs and small fish. Widespread throughout tropical Indo-Pacific, south to northern KwaZulu-Natal. A relatively common kingfish.

Shrimp scad

Coastal kingfish

Yellowspotted kingfish

Giant kingfish

Rainbow runner

Golden kingfish (sub-adult)

GARRICK (LEERVIS) – *Lichia amia*
Can attain 150 cm. A large fish with an elongated body, which is deepest opposite the first dorsal and anal fins. Has a slightly pointed snout. The overall body colour is silvery, but the upper sides are dusky to blue-grey, while the underside is white. Also has a prominent wavy lateral line, dark fins and lacks scutes. Small juveniles are yellow with several black crossbars. Ranges in depth from 1-20 m. An aggressive coastal predator that is extremely agile and is able to hunt fish in the dynamic surf zone along sandy beaches and rocky points. Usually hunts in groups for fish such as mullet, pinkies and sardine. Distribution ranges from the Mediterranean Sea, southwards to the West African coast and around the Cape to northern KwaZulu-Natal. Migrates north to KwaZulu-Natal to spawn, following the winter sardine run. Common but rarely seen by divers. Much prized by shore-anglers and spearfishermen.

WHITE KINGFISH (SILVER TREVALLY) – *Pseudocaranx dentex*
Attains 96 cm. This conspicuous kingfish has an elongated body with a smoothly curved upper and lower body profile, and a fairly straight forehead. Its main distinguishing features are the yellow mid-lateral stripe, the yellow dorsal and tail fins, and the black spot on the gill cover. Dorsally the body colour is greenish blue, and changes to a silvery white ventrally. Occurs singly or in small groups near offshore reefs to a depth of 200 m. Diet comprises bottom-living invertebrates and small fish. This species is found on both sides of the Atlantic, in the Mediterranean Sea and the Indo-Pacific. It is fairly common on northern KwaZulu-Natal reefs.

TALANG QUEENFISH (LARGE MOUTH QUEENFISH) – *Scomberoides commersonnianus*
Attains 120 cm. This species is readily identified by its elongated mackerel-shaped body, blunt snout, large mouth and the five to eight large distinct blotches along the sides of the body. Overall colour is silvery, but may be dusky-green dorsally. This fish lacks scutes on the lateral line, and the dorsal and anal fins are venomous. Swims in small groups and frequents coastal reefs and rocky pinnacles to a depth of 80 m. Sometimes enters estuaries. This pelagic predator feeds on small bottom-living fishes, crabs and squid. Widespread throughout Indian Ocean from the Eastern Cape northwards, also occurs off Taiwan and Australia. An uncommon species rarely seen by divers.

SOUTHERN POMPANO (AFRICAN POMPANO) – *Trachinotus africanus*
Attains 90 cm. The body is large and robust, lacking spots or scutes on the sides. Has a distinctive blunt nose. Overall colour is silvery with a bluish back and a white underside. Fins are dusky yellow, and the tail is strongly forked. Inhabits shallow coastal waters in the vicinity of reefs and rocky outcrops, as well as along sandy shores, to a depth of 30 m. A shoaling species that feeds predominantly on mussels and mole crabs, which are crushed with its strong pharyngeal grinding plates. Occurs from Knysna northwards to Mozambique, Gulf of Aden, Oman and the eastern Indian Ocean. Common but rarely seen by divers and often caught by shore anglers in the surf-zone.

SNUBNOSE POMPANO (SILVER POMPANO) – *Trachinotus blochii*
Attains 65 cm. This species can be distinguished by its blunt nose and oval-shaped body, which lacks markings and scutes. Although generally silvery in colour, the upper surface is bluish and the underside is sometimes yellowish. The fins are dusky yellow and the anal fin has a brown tip. Juveniles frequent shallow sandy inshore and estuary areas, whilst adults shoal on shallow coastal reefs to a depth of 50 m. Feeds mainly on bottom-dwelling prey such as molluscs and other hard-shelled invertebrates, which are crushed by its strong pharyngeal teeth. Widespread throughout Indo-West Pacific, Red Sea, south to central KwaZulu-Natal. Generally less common than the southern pompano.

LARGE SPOTTED POMPANO (MOONFISH) – *Trachinotus botla*
Attains 60 cm. Characteristic features include its robust oval-shaped body, the blunt snout and three to four large black spots on the sides. The body colour is silvery, and bluish dorsally. The fin lobes are dark blue. It lacks scutes on the lateral-line. This fast swimming, agile fish prefers the turbulent surf-zone along sandy beaches and even swims on its side to enter very shallow water. Ranges in depth from 0,3-50 m. Feeds almost exclusively on mole crabs, but clams and sand-mussels are also eaten. Occurs from the Eastern Cape, northwards to Kenya, Madagascar, Sri Lanka and western Australia. Common off the beaches of KwaZulu-Natal and Mozambique.

Garrick

White kingfish

Talang queenfish

Southern pompano

Snubnose pompano

Large spotted pompano

LONGFIN YELLOWTAIL (TROPICAL YELLOWTAIL OR ALMACO JACK) – *Seriola rivoliana*
Attains 70 cm. A moderately elongated fish with a smoothly curved upper profile. The overall colour is silvery-olive with paler lower sides. Best recognized by the yellow-brown bar running at an angle across the head and a similar coloured longitudinal stripe on the side of the body. Has noticeably short pectoral fins. Fins are generally dusky except for the anal fin, which is edged in white. Usually found in small to large groups swimming over offshore reefs as well as in oceanic waters. Ranges in depth from 15-70 m. An aggressive predator of small fish. Widely distributed throughout Indo-Pacific, extending south to the Eastern Cape. A common fish that is often drawn to diver's bubbles.

CAPE YELLOWTAIL (GIANT YELLOWTAIL OR YELLOWTAIL AMBERJACK) – *Seriola lalandi*
Attains 150 cm but rarely exceeds 100 cm. This large gamefish has a torpedo-shaped body, small fins and a large forked yellow tail fin. The body colour is blue-green dorsally, and silvery-white ventrally, with a horizontal yellow or bronze stripe along its side from snout to tail. Found in most temperate and subtropical seas. This gregarious predator occurs in very large shoals in coastal and offshore waters and is often found around pinnacles. Ranges in depth from 2-50 m. Preys mainly on shoaling fishes such as pilchards, mackerel and anchovy, but also feeds on pelagic crustaceans and squid. Most common in Atlantic waters, but each winter migrates up the East Coast to KwaZulu-Natal, following the sardine run. An important part of the commercial line-fish catches in the Western Cape.

MAASBANKER (HORSE MACKEREL) – *Trachurus trachurus*
Attains 70 cm but rarely exceeds 40 cm. Overall silvery colour with an olive-green dorsal surface and a black spot on the gill cover. This small fish has large eyes and a distinctive lateral line, which slopes steeply midway along the body. 75 enlarged scales forming spiky scutes are arranged along the lateral line. The maasbanker occurs in huge shoals from shallow water to depths of 400 m. Feeds on plankton strained from the water through its gill rakers. Ranges from southern Mozambique, around the Western Cape to Norway. Generally a common fish and an important prey species for dolphins, seals and sharks. Commercially harvested in large quantities in the Western Cape.

Knifejaws – Family Oplegnathidae
Knifejaws are a small family distributed throughout warmer seas. They are especially prevalent in southern Africa, Japan and Australia. These species are characterized by an enlarged second dorsal fin, small compact scales, and teeth that are fused together forming a parrot-like beak. Adults are usually drab and dark in colour, while juveniles can be colourful. Three species occur off the east coast of southern Africa, and all are commonly found on coastal reefs.

NATAL KNIFEJAW – *Oplegnathus robinsoni*
Attains 60 cm. A robust, deep-bodied fish with an overall brown or grey colour. Juveniles are bright yellow with black crossbars. Occurs singly or in pairs. Frequents coral and rocky reefs at depths of 10-100 m. The powerful beak is used to scrape encrusting organisms such as sponges, corals and red-bait off the reef. This endemic species ranges from Mocambique to KwaZulu-Natal, and is particularly abundant on the reefs off KwaZulu-Natal. It is an inquisitive fish and readily approaches divers.

Remoras – Family Echeneidae
This unusual group of slender fishes has a laminar sucking disc on top of a flattened head, used to attach themselves to larger fishes, turtles, mammals and even ships. These sea-going hitch-hikers feed on scraps from their feeding hosts and some may remove parasitic crustaceans from their host. Some remoras are species-specific with regard to their hosts.

SHARK REMORA (SHARKSUCKER OR SLENDER SUCKERFISH) – *Echeneis naucrates*
Attains 100 cm. This species has a very slender white body with a broad black stripe along its side from the tip of the lower jaw to the tail. The stripe may fade on large adults. The dorsal surface is often grey. Generally associated with sharks, rays, large fish and turtles. Occasionally seen swimming alone. Ranges in depth from 3-45 m. Feeds on host parasites and left over scraps of food eaten by its host. This fish is encountered in all warm seas throughout the world. Juveniles may follow or even attach themselves to divers.

Longfin yellowtail

Cape yellowtail

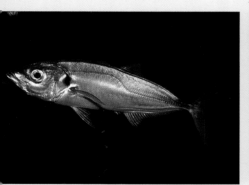

Maasbanker

Natal knifejaw

Natal knifejaw (juvenile)

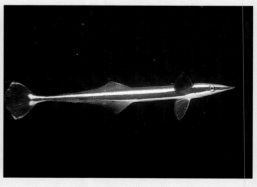

Shark remora

Hawkfishes – Family Cirrhitidae

Hawkfishes are small colourful bottom-dwelling fishes, that are characterized by a single, deeply notched dorsal fin with minute tassel-like filaments at the tip of each dorsal spine. Often found perched on coral heads and sponges, using stout pectoral fins for balance. They make periodic dashes when capturing prey.

MARBLED HAWKFISH (STOCKY HAWKFISH) – *Cirrhitus pinnulatus*
Attains 28 cm. The largest member of the hawkfish family. The body colour is greenish brown with three rows of white spots and numerous smaller dark brown spots on the sides. The underside is white. This inshore species is confined to rocky shores and shallow reefs exposed to surge. Ranges in depth from 1-5 m. Feeds on small fish and crustaceans. Widespread throughout Indo-Pacific, south to the Eastern Cape. An uncommon species.

Fingerfins – Family Cheilodaclylidae

Fingerfins are a small family of bottom-dwelling fish that inhabit the cooler waters of southern Africa, South America, New Zealand and Australia. They are characterized by an oblong body and enlarged pectoral fins, which are used for balance while 'lying' on the seabed. The mouth is small and the lips fleshy.

BARRED FINGERFIN – *Cheilodactylus pixi*
Attains 25 cm. Readily distinguished by its whitish body with five dark brown crossbars extending onto the dorsal fin. Numerous tiny dark blotches are scattered over the pale areas between the bars. The fins are pale yellow, except for the translucent spinous dorsal fin. Frequents rocky shores and offshore reefs in depths of 5-50 m. Diet consists of small invertebrates such as worms, crabs and shellfish. An endemic species known only from Knysna in the Western Cape to southern KwaZulu-Natal. Relatively common.

Damselfishes – Family Pomacentridae

Damselfishes form one of the largest families of reef fishes inhabiting coastal waters. These small fishes have moderately deep, compressed bodies and vary greatly in colour and pattern. Damselfishes display interesting behaviour. Most species, especially algae-feeders, are territorial and aggressive towards intruders, particularly when adults are guarding their nesting sites. Females lay their eggs on a hard substrate, which is thoroughly cleaned beforehand. Eggs are attached to the substrate by adhesive strands. The eggs are usually guarded by the male. Some species occur singly, whilst others form large aggregations.

BANDED SERGEANT (SEVENBAR DAMSEL) – *Abudefduf septemfasciatus*
Attains 19 cm. Distinguished by six dark grey, vertical bars on a pale yellow body. Sometimes the sixth bar on the head is indistinct. The bars darken during mating displays and mood changes. Juveniles inhabit the intertidal area and are often found in tidal-pools. A highly territorial and aggressive fish, which is found along rocky shores and on shallow reefs exposed to wave action in depths of 0,3-4 m. Feeds on algae and small invertebrates. Widespread throughout tropical Indo-West Pacific, extending to southern KwaZulu-Natal. A common species, similar to the spot damsel, *Abudefdus sordidus*, but lacks the black spot on the caudal fin base.

FALSE-EYE DAMSEL – *Abudefduf sparoides*
Attains 16 cm. This species has an overall metallic blue colour with several rows of small light blue spots on the upper body and a large prominent black blotch at the base of the tail. Juveniles are sometimes found in tidal-pools. Encountered singly or in loose groups. Inhabits rocky shores and shallow coral reefs exposed to moderate wave action. Ranges in depth from 0,3-3 m. Feeds on algae and small invertebrates. Known from the Eastern Cape to Kenya, Aldabra, Mauritius, Reunion and Madagascar. A relatively uncommon species.

DOUBLEBAR CHROMIS – *Chromis opercularis*
Attains 16 cm. One of the largest members of the *Chromis* genus. Some geographical variations in colour may occur, which makes identification difficult. In southern Africa, juveniles are greyish blue with black edges to the scales and a bright yellow tail. The rear of the soft dorsal and anal fins are black and it has a distinctive double black bar on the head. Adults are similar, but the body colour is greyish blue above and yellowish grey below and the tail changes to a dusky colour. Juveniles are usually found swimming in small groups close to the reef. Adults occur singly or in pairs. Inhabits inshore and offshore coral reefs, ranging in depth from 4-40 m. Prefers current prone reefs and feeds on zooplankton. Occurs throughout the tropical Indian Ocean extending south to the KwaZulu-Natal south coast. Relatively common.

Marbled hawkfish

Barred fingerfin

Banded sergeant

False-eye damsel

Doublebar chromis

Doublebar chromis (juvenile)

YELLOW CHROMIS – *Chromis analis*

Attains 15 cm. This fish has an oval shaped, yellowish-brown body which is darker above and lighter below, and a distinctive white tail. The tips of the dorsal fin spines are orange. Occurs singly or in pairs. It is encountered on moderately deep offshore reefs ranging in depth from 20-70 m. Feeds on zooplankton above the reef. Distribution ranges from Indonesia to Fiji, Red Sea and the western Indian Ocean, extending to southern KwaZulu-Natal. Relatively uncommon and rarely seen shallower than 25 m in southern Africa waters.

BROWN CHROMIS (SCALY CHROMIS) – *Chromis lepidolepis*

Attains 8 cm. This small damselfish is greyish brown overall with black and white tips to the dorsal fin spines, and a vertical black bar across the eye. The upper and lower trailing edges of the tail fin are dusky, with black lobes. Encountered singly or in small groups and is usually found close to shelter. Favours reef crests and slopes on inshore and offshore reefs to a depth of 20 m. Diet consists mainly of zooplankton. Widespread throughout tropical Indo-Pacific to the Fiji Islands, Red Sea, extending to southern KwaZulu-Natal. Common on reefs off northern KwaZulu-Natal.

CRESCENT DAMSEL (REGAL DEMOISELLE) – *Neopomacentrus cyanomos*

Attains 10 cm. Overall dark brown in colour with a light blue spot on each body scale, and bright yellow areas on the rear of the dorsal and anal fins, and the trailing edges of the tail fin. A prominent dark green to black spot is located on the upper edge of the gill cover. Some geographical colour variations are known to occur with this species. Usually observed singly or in small loose groups. Frequents inshore and offshore reefs and shipwrecks ranging in depth from 5-30 m. Diet comprises mainly zooplankton. Widespread throughout Indian Ocean, Red Sea and northern Australia, extending to southern KwaZulu-Natal. An uncommon species.

NARROWBAR DAMSEL – *Plectroglyphidodon dickii*

Attains 11 cm. Identified by the black narrow bar across the rear of the body, followed by a white tail in juveniles and a yellow tail in adults. The body is tan coloured and each scale has a brown border. Generally a solitary species, but may occur in small loose groups. Found amongst the branches of *Pocillopora* and *Acropora* coral. Tends to flit from one coral or rock to another. Frequents rocky and coral reefs, often in the surge zone, to a depth of between 2-15 m. Feeds primarily on filamentous algae and small bottom-living invertebrates. Widespread throughout tropical Indo-West Pacific extending to southern KwaZulu-Natal. This highly territorial species is relatively common.

WIDEBAR DAMSEL (JOHNSTON DAMSEL) – *Plectroglyphidodon johnstonianus*

Attains 9 cm. This moderately small damselfish has a pale tan to pale yellowish body colour and a broad black, almost oval shaped, bar across the rear of the body. Occasionally this black marking is absent. The scales are marked with indistinct pale blue spots. Occurs singly or in pairs. Generally, it is found among the branches of *Pocillopora*, *Acropora* or *Stylophora* corals and is usually only seen when it darts from one coral to another. Favours exposed coral reefs to a depth of 18 m. Diet consists of algae, small invertebrates and coral polyps. Widespread throughout tropical Indo-West Pacific to Hawaii extending to southern KwaZulu-Natal. A relatively common species. This damsel is similar to the narrowbar damsel, *Plectroglyphidodon dickii*, which has a narrower well defined black bar and is more brown in colour.

JEWEL DAMSEL – *Plectroglyphidodon lacrymatus*

Attains 10 cm. This attractive damselfish is readily identified by its overall brown colour with tiny bright blue spots scattered over the upper half of the body. The blue spots are less evident in large adults. The iris of the eyes is yellow. Generally found in areas of mixed coral and algae covered rubble. Occurs singly or in pairs. Feeds on algae and small invertebrates. Inhabits shallow tropical lagoons and offshore coral reefs in depths ranging from 1-40 m. Widespread throughout tropical Indo-West Pacific, south to KwaZulu-Natal. A relatively common species.

Yellow chromis

Brown chromis

Crescent damsel

Narrowbar damsel

Widebar damsel

Jewel damsel

SULPHUR DAMSEL (LEMON DAMSEL) – *Pomacentrus sulfureus*

Attains 11 cm. This unmistakable damselfish is bright yellow with a prominent black spot at the base of the pectoral fin. Occurs singly or in pairs, frequenting shallow coral reefs ranging in depth from 1-10 m. Generally remains close to its shelter. Feeds on zooplankton, algae and small invertebrates. Distribution includes the Red Sea, the East African coast south to Mozambique, Seychelles and Mauritius. An uncommon species.

SAPPHIRE DAMSEL (BLUE OR AZURE DAMSEL) – *Pomacentrus pavo*

Attains 11 cm. The body colour of this attractive damselfish varies from pale blue-green to light blue. Some individuals have ornate streaks, spots and lines as shown in the photograph. Usually has a small blue ear-spot. Large adults may have yellow pectoral fins and yellow on the rear half of the tail fin, but this is variable. Forms small to large aggregations and is commonly seen darting in and out of corals. It is generally found around coral outcrops in tropical lagoons and on inshore reefs at depths of between 1-16 m. Feeds on zooplankton and filamentous algae. Widespread throughout the Indo-Pacific, ranging south to northern KwaZulu-Natal. A common species.

YELLOWTAIL DAMSEL – *Pomacentrus trichourus*

Attains 10 cm. This damsel is identified by its dark blue to charcoal coloured body and the distinctive tri-coloured tail, which is black at the base, yellow in the middle and has a pale rear margin. Also has a blue ear-spot. Usually encountered singly. Frequents inshore and offshore coral reefs to depths of between 1-30 m. Lives close to the bottom and feeds primarily on algae and small invertebrates. Widespread throughout the western Indian Ocean, Red Sea extending south to northern KwaZulu-Natal. Generally an uncommon and rather shy species.

REDWING CORAL DAMSEL (FUSILIER DAMSEL) – *Lepidozygus tapeinosoma*

Attains 10 cm. This unusually elongate damselfish is metallic green on the upper surface, becoming yellowish towards the rear. The lower sides and belly are pinkish and sometimes bluish. Has a prominent yellow mark on the rear of the dorsal fin. Has been reported to change colour when feeding. Occurs on offshore coral and rocky reefs, ranging in depth from 10-30 m. Feeds on zooplankton. Widespread throughout tropical Indo-West Pacific, extending to southern KwaZulu-Natal. A relatively common damsel that is usually found swimming among threadfin goldies, *Nemanthias carberryi,* which are similar in colour and body shape.

Wrasses – Family Labridae

Wrasses are a large, diverse family of reef fishes that vary considerably in size and shape. The majority are small and elongate, and have a continuous unnotched dorsal fin. Their mouths are relatively small and often have projecting front teeth. Many are beautifully coloured and some exhibit dramatic changes in colour patterns between phases, which include juvenile, initial (subadult) and terminal (sexually mature adult) phases. Initial phase individuals and terminal females often have a similar colour pattern. Females are able to change sex to become terminal males. Wrasses have a distinct swimming style that depends more on the pectoral fins than the tail. All wrasses are carnivorous, but their food items vary. They have strong grinding plates deep in their gullet, used for crushing hard-shelled prey. Wrasses are inactive at night, the smaller ones often sleep beneath the sand for protection. Among the largest of the wrasses are those of the genus *Bodianus*, which are commonly called hogfishes.

BLUESPOTTED TAMARIN – *Anampses caeruleopunctatus*

Attains 30 cm. Initial phase individuals are overall orange-brown with horizontal rows of small dark-edged blue spots on the body and fins, and dark-edged narrow blue lines on the head, sometimes radiating from the eye. Terminal males become deep bodied and are blue with an olive-green head and a distinctive light green bar across the body to the rear of the pectoral fin. Small juveniles have pale olive or brownish mottled coloration. Juveniles mimic floating seaweed to avoid detection and are commonly known as leaf wrasses. This wrasse occurs either singly, in pairs or in small groups, usually with an adult male nearby. Buries itself in the sand at night for safety, or if threatened. This fish is found on inshore and offshore reefs at depths of 10-60 m, but are more abundant on shallow coral reefs exposed to surge. An energetic swimmer that forages continuously for worms and small crustaceans. Ranges throughout Indo-Pacific, Red Sea, extending to southern KwaZulu-Natal. A common species.

Sulphur damsel

Sapphire damsel

Yellowtail damsel

Redwing coral damsel

Bluespotted tamarin (initial phase)

Bluespotted tamarin (juvenile)

YELLOWTAIL TAMARIN (YELLOWTAIL WRASSE OR SPOTTED WRASSE)
– *Anampses meleagrides*
Attains 22 cm. Initial phase individuals and terminal females are similar in colour pattern and are identified by their conspicuous bright yellow tail and the dark brown body. A small white spot marks each scale. The head, dorsal and anal fins are also spotted. Terminal males are reddish brown with a short vertical blue line on each scale. The head and thorax have irregular blue lines. The tail fin is orange with dark-edged blue spots and a white posterior crescent, preceded by a narrow blue band. Inhabits offshore coral reefs, especially areas of mixed coral, rubble and sand. Buries itself under the sand at night or when threatened. Ranges in depth from 5-60 m. Females often form small loose groups and are constantly on the move, stopping only to feed. Diet consists of small fishes and bottom-living invertebrates. Widespread throughout Indo-West Pacific, Red Sea, south to southern KwaZulu-Natal. A common species. The photograph shows both terminal male and initial phase individuals.

YELLOWBREASTED WRASSE – *Anampses twistii*
Attains 18 cm. In contrast to other members of this genus, terminal males and females are similar in colour pattern. A distinctive yellow area extends from the belly to the mouth. The body, upper head, dorsal and anal fins are dark brown and covered with numerous small black-edged blue spots. A large blue-edged black spot occurs at the rear of both the dorsal and anal fins. Juveniles are olive-brown with numerous light blue spots and irregular short lines on head and body. The large false eyespots at the rear of the dorsal and anal fins are very prominent on juveniles. Occurs in tropical lagoons and on offshore coral and rocky reefs. Buries itself under the sand at night for safety. Never strays far from the protection of the reef. Ranges in depth from 10-30 m. Feeds on bottom-living invertebrates. Widespread throughout Indo-West Pacific, Red Sea, extending to southern KwaZulu-Natal. A relatively common species.

LINED WRASSE – *Anampses lineatus*
Attains 12 cm. The difference between the initial and terminal phases of both sexes is not marked, however the juveniles are radically different. Terminal females have an orange-brown body with pale yellowish spots on the head, and rows of white elongated spots that form dashed lines along the body. The tail is banded in black and white. Terminal males have a similar pattern but the colour of the spots and dashed lines are bluish. Juveniles are black with numerous pale yellow spots and irregular circular type markings. The dorsal fin margin is whitish and joins a white band on the tail. Also has a narrow white bar across the body at the rear of the pectoral fin. Encountered on offshore coral and rocky reefs ranging in depths from 18-42 m. Feeds on bottom-dwelling invertebrates. Ranges throughout the Indian Ocean, east to Indonesia and south to KwaZulu-Natal. A common species.

NATAL WRASSE – *Anchichoerops natalensis*
Attains 70 cm. This large robust wrasse is either reddish with yellow or orange spots, or orange-yellow to brown with darker spots. Seven to ten dark vertical bars are usually present on the sides, but these tend to fade with age. A thin blue margin is usually present on the median fins. The lips are fleshy and protrusible. Tends to be sluggish, swimming leisurely along the outer edges of reefs and rocky headlands to depths of at least 55 m. Diet comprises sponges, ascidians, corals, crabs and crayfish. An endemic species known only from the Eastern Cape and KwaZulu-Natal. An uncommon species protected by law in KwaZulu-Natal from being caught by spearfishermen.

LINED HOGFISH – *Bodianus trilineatus*
Attains 25 cm. The upper body is pale red, changing to creamy yellow on lower sides. Five stripes extend along the sides. The upper three are red and black, while the lower pair is plain red. Sometimes an undefined yellow stripe occurs mid-laterally along the body. Both sexes have a similar colour. Found singly or in pairs. Seeks shelter at night in holes or crevices in the reef. Inhabits offshore reefs ranging in depth from 25-50 m. Feeds on gastropods, bivalve molluscs and coral polyps, which are crushed by its strong grinding plates. Occurs along the East African coast from Kenya to southern KwaZulu-Natal. Generally uncommon, but occasionally sighted on deeper reefs off the south coast of KwaZulu-Natal.

Yellowtail tamarin (initial phase) in background,
Bluespotted tamarin in foreground

Yellowbreasted wrasse

Lined wrasse

Lined wrasse (juvenile)

Natal wrasse

Lined hogfish

LYRETAIL HOGFISH – *Bodianus anthioides*
Attains 21 cm. There is very little difference in the colour pattern between males, females and juveniles of this species. The lyretail hogfish has a curved upper head profile and a lunate tail fin, which is particularly prominent in juveniles. The head and front third of the body is orange-brown and the remainder is white, with scattered irregular dark brown spots. Has a black spot at the front of the dorsal fin and dark brown margins to the tail fin, which continue onto the caudal peduncle. Generally occurs singly, swimming close to the reef. Small juveniles sometimes shelter in large bush-like black corals or sponges. Usually found along outer slopes of offshore reefs in depths of 10-40 m. Feeds primarily on small shelled invertebrates, especially shrimps and worms. Widespread throughout Indo-Pacific, Red Sea, extending to southern KwaZulu-Natal. Uncommon in southern African waters.

TWOSPOT HOGFISH (TWOSPOT SLENDER HOGFISH) – *Bodianus bimaculatus*
Attains 10 cm. One of the smallest of the *Bodianus* genus, characterized by its brightly coloured slender body. Both sexes are bright yellowish orange in colour with a pale underside. A broad red stripe runs mid-laterally along the body from the eye to the tail. A conspicuous yellow-edged black or blue spot is present on the upper gill cover while a small red spot is sometimes visible at the base of the tail. Terminal males have an additional red line on the back. Occurs singly or in small groups. Inhabits rubble and sandy areas at the base of reefs to depths of 28-60 m. Preys on small bottom-living invertebrates. Ranges from the western Pacific to Mauritius, Maldives and Mozambique, extending to southern KwaZulu-Natal. Moderately common on the deeper offshore reefs, off the south coast of KwaZulu-Natal.

TWOSPOT WRASSE – *Oxycheilinus bimaculatus*
Attains 15 cm. One of the smallest wrasses of the genus *Oxycheilinus*. This wrasse has variable body coloration, but is mostly reddish brown or greenish brown with a pale throat and underside. It is characterized by its unusually shaped tail fin, which has extended top and middle ray filaments, giving the tail a ragged appearance. Juveniles have an evenly rounded tail fin. Initial phase individuals have a broad dark, lateral stripe on the side, which breaks into blotches in adults. Both have short greenish lines on the head, some radiating from the eye. Does not change greatly in colour with growth or between phases. Occurs singly or in pairs on reefs with dense algae growth or in seagrass beds. Ranging from the surge-zone to a depth of 40 m. Its mottled colour pattern makes it difficult to spot amongst the growth on the reef. Feeds on bottom-dwelling invertebrates. Widespread in the Indo-Pacific, extending to southern KwaZulu-Natal. A fairly common species.

CHEEKLINED WRASSE (BANDCHEEK WRASSE) – *Oxycheilinus digramma*
Attains 35 cm. The coloration is variable but generally has a pale green head and dorsal surface, and a reddish-brown underside. Each scale is marked with an orange-red bar. Other features include pink scribbles on the head and several diagonal pink or maroon lines on the cheek. Usually solitary and often swims well above the reef. Reported to swim with groups of goatfish, changing its colour to resemble these fish, and darting out occasionally in order to capture small fish. Found on coral reefs, ranging in depth from 3-30 m. Diet consists of bottom-living invertebrates and fish. Widespread throughout Indo-Pacific, Red Sea, south to northern KwaZulu-Natal. An uncommon species.

RED-BANDED WRASSE (RED-BREASTED SPLENDOUR WRASSE) – *Cheilinus fasciatus*
Attains 38 cm. Terminal males and females have a similar colour pattern. The front third of the body is yellowish orange and the head is greyish green. The rear two thirds of the body is charcoal coloured and broadly banded with whitish crossbars extending to the tail. Also has a vertical black streak on each scale. Large canines are present in the front of its jaws, which is typical of the *Cheilinus* genus. Found singly in tropical lagoons and on seaward coral reefs, preferring areas of mixed coral, rubble and sand. Ranges in depth from 4-40 m. Preys on bottom-living invertebrates and small fish. Widespread throughout Indo-Pacific, Red Sea, south to central Mozambique. A relatively common species.

Lyretail hogfish

Lyretail hogfish (juvenile)

Twospot hogfish (initial phase)

Twospot wrasse

Cheeklined wrasse

Red-banded wrasse

TRIPLETAIL WRASSE – *Cheilinus trilobatus*
Attains 45 cm. Adults of both sexes are similar in appearance and are identified by a moderately large, deep body and distinctive three pronged tail. The general body colour is olive to brown with close-set, short vertical pinkish lines on the body, and two whitish bands across the caudal peduncle. The head is covered with fine pink dots and scribbles. Juveniles and initial phase individuals are similar in colour to adults, but have additional whitish bands on the body and a rounded tail fin. Occurs singly, frequenting shallow to moderately deep coral reefs, ranging in depth from 1-40 m. Preys on small fishes, crustaceans and molluscs. Widespread throughout Indo-Pacific south to northern KwaZulu-Natal. This uncommon wrasse tends to be wary of divers.

HUMPHEAD WRASSE (NAPOLEON WRASSE) – *Cheilinus undulatus*
Attains 230 cm. One of the best known of the wrasse family and a favourite with divers. It is one of the largest of reef fishes, weighing up to 190 kg. Large adults have a prominent hump on forehead. Overall colour pattern of both sexes is olive to green, with a dark vertical bar on each scale forming almost vertical lines on the body. Two black lines extend backwards from the rear of the eye. This mostly solitary species inhabits tropical lagoons and offshore coral reefs. Adults regularly patrol the reef in search for prey. Usually sleeps in a cave at night. Occasionally found on shipwrecks. Small juveniles live in weedy areas and are rarely seen. Depth ranges from 1-60 m. Feeds on a variety of small fishes, molluscs, sea-urchins, crustaceans and other invertebrates. Widespread throughout Indo-Pacific, Red Sea, south to Inhaca Island, Mozambique. This uncommon species is often wary, except when fed by divers. Unfortunately they are now being commercially exploited for food in some areas of the Indian Ocean.

CIGAR WRASSE – *Cheilio inermis*
Attains 50 cm. This slender, cigar-shaped wrasse may be plain yellow, green or brown. It sometimes has a narrow mid-lateral broken black stripe together with a pale stripe along the dorsal surface from the snout to the tail. Terminal males lack the stripes and develop a large irregular orange to salmon-pink area on upper side of body behind the gill cover. Favours open substrates with seagrass or dense algae growth, but is also found on offshore reefs to a depth of over 30 m. Feeds on molluscs, hermit-crabs, crabs, sea urchins and shrimps. Widespread throughout Indo-Pacific, Red Sea, extending to southern KwaZulu-Natal. An uncommon species.

EXQUISITE WRASSE – *Cirrhilabrus exquisitus*
Attains 11 cm. Terminal males and females are similar in coloration and have a complex colour pattern comprising areas of green, red and blue with a black spot at the base of the tail. Juveniles are purple overall with numerous tiny blue spots scattered over head and body. They also have a black spot at the base of the tail, and a white spot on the snout. Males are territorial and form large harems. During courtship, males display brilliant hues to attract females. Inhabits offshore reefs, where juveniles are found close to sand and rubble bottoms, while adults prefer reef tops, where they usually form loose aggregations. Found at depths ranging from 6-32 m. Feeds on zooplankton. Widespread throughout Indo-Pacific, extending to southern KwaZulu-Natal. A moderately common species.

STRIATED WRASSE – *Pseudocheilinus evanidus*
Attains 8 cm. A small wrasse with an overall orange to pinkish-brown colour and closely spaced pale longitudinal lines on the body. Sometimes pale bands are present on the body. Best recognized by the bluish-white streak extending along the mouth to the cheek. All phases appear to have a similar colour pattern. Generally occurs singly, living close to the reef for protection. Found on moderately deep offshore reefs at depths of 15-40 m. Diet consists mainly of small bottom-dwelling invertebrates. Widespread throughout Indo-Pacific, extending to southern KwaZulu-Natal. A fairly common, yet rather secretive, wrasse.

Tripletail wrasse

Humphead wrasse

Cigar wrasse

Exquisite wrasse

Exquisite wrasse (juvenile)

Striated wrasse

SIXSTRIPE WRASSE – *Pseudocheilinus hexataenia*

Attains 7 cm. This small colourful wrasse is readily identified by its purple body with numerous orange lines along the sides, yellow dots on the throat and a pale green tail. All phases have a similar colour pattern. Usually occurs singly, but may form small groups. Inhabits coral and rocky offshore reefs to depths of 5-35 m. Never ventures far from its coral or rubble shelter. More abundant in rich coral areas. Feeds on small, bottom-living invertebrates. Widespread throughout Indo-Pacific, Red Sea, extending to southern KwaZulu-Natal. A common yet secretive wrasse.

SLINGJAW WRASSE – *Epibulus insidiator*

Attains 35 cm. This unusual wrasse has a protractible jaw that when extended, forms a tube about half the length of its body, hence the common name. Initial phase and terminal females are uniform yellow or brown in colour. Terminal males have a distinctive greyish-green body with a dark green edge on the body scales and a diffuse yellow bar to the rear of the pectoral fin. Also has an orange-red area below the front of the dorsal fin and a light grey head, with black lines radiating from the eyes. The upper and lower filaments of the tail fin and the tip of the anal fin are greatly extended in adults. Lives singly or in pairs in coral-rich areas of tropical lagoons and seaward coral reefs at depths of between 4-40 m. Uses its long extendible tubular mouth to probe the reef for small coral-dwelling fishes, shrimps and crabs. Distributed throughout Indo-Pacific, Red Sea, south to central Mozambique. Relatively common.

PICTURE WRASSE (NEBULOUS WRASSE) – *Halichoeres nebulosus*

Attains 12 cm. Colours vary with habitat and geographical location, ranging from mottled green to brown or pink. The terminal female has an irregular dark crossbar midway along the body and a pinkish-red area on the belly. Also has a small oblong shaped black spot behind the eye and a yellow-edged black spot midway along the dorsal fin. Terminal males are primarily mottled green, with the pinkish area on the belly reduced or absent, and the black spot less defined or absent. Both phases have pink lines on the head. Juveniles have similar colours to adults. Primarily an inshore species with adults and juveniles frequently found on shallow reefs, especially in surge areas with good algal growth. Also occurs on offshore reefs to a depth of 40 m. Preys on bottom-living invertebrates and small fishes. Widespread throughout Indo-Pacific, Red Sea, south to the Eastern Cape. A common species.

ZIGZAG SANDWRASSE – *Halichoeres scalpularis*

Attains 20 cm. Initial phase and terminal females are readily identified by the black zigzag stripe along the sides from eye to tail. The colour of the stripe is variable and can be yellow or lavender-pink, but usually begins as black on the head. The general colour is greenish dorsally and whitish below. Terminal males are uniform green with a bolder lavender-pink zigzag stripe and pink vertical lines on scales. The head has irregular lavender-pink markings. This species is common in sandy areas near reef edges and over seagrass beds. Sometimes follows goatfishes or emperors to feed on creatures disturbed in the sand. Often seen in loose groups with a single, large, colourful male. Ranges in depth from the intertidal zone to at least 50 m. Feeds on bottom-dwelling invertebrates. Widespread throughout Indo-West Pacific, Red Sea, south to northern KwaZulu-Natal. A common wrasse.

BARRED RINGWRASSE – *Hologymnosus annulatus*

Attains 40 cm. Initial phase and terminal females are brown to olive-brown with a banded pattern of narrow black bars along the sides. Terminal males are green, shading to blue-green on lower sides with a banded pattern of narrow purple bars and blue-green lines on the head. Sometimes has a narrow pale crossbar midway along body. Juveniles are pale yellow with a broad dark brown to black stripe along lower side from snout to tail. Frequents offshore coral reefs usually on reef tops and slopes to a depth of 30 m. Juveniles prefer areas of mixed rubble, sand and coral. A solitary wrasse that feeds on small fishes and crustaceans. Widespread throughout Indo-Pacific, Red Sea, extending to northern KwaZulu-Natal. Juveniles are more commonly seen than adults.

Sixstripe wrasse

Slingjaw wrasse (terminal male)

Slingjaw wrasse (initial phase)

Picture wrasse (terminal male)

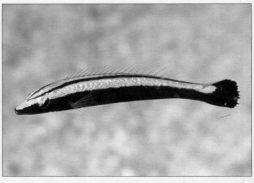

Zigzag sandwrasse (initial phase)

Barred ringwrasse (juvenile)

BICOLOUR CLEANER WRASSE – *Labroides bicolor*
Attains 14 cm. Terminal adults have a dark blue head and a black body changing abruptly to yellow, which extends posteriorly onto the tail. The end of the tail is black with a pale margin. Juveniles are black with a bright yellow stripe along the back from snout to tail. Juveniles and initial phase individuals often occur at cleaning stations at specific areas on the reef. Adults are more inclined to roam over the reef in pursuit of customers that need to be cleaned. Cleaner wrasses safely enter the mouths of larger fish without fear of being eaten. To advertise their trade, they swim in a distinctive up-and-down motion. Feeds mainly on external parasites and diseased or damaged tissues of other fish. Ranges in depth from 2-30 m. Widely distributed throughout Indo-Pacific, extending to southern KwaZulu-Natal. A relatively common species.

DIVIDED WRASSE (VERMICULATE WRASSE) – *Macropharyngodon bipartitus*
Attains 11 cm. This striking wrasse exhibits a marked difference between phases. Initial phase and terminal females are orange with numerous pale blue spots covering the body and fins, and have a large black area covering the chest and belly. The head is pale yellow with black-edged orange spots and scribbles. Terminal males are a dull orange with dark-edged pale green spots or short irregular lines on body and head. Prefers mixed coral, sand and rubble areas, and lives close to the seabed. Females often form small groups while males maintain harems. Inhabits tropical lagoons and offshore reefs to depths of 1-30 m. Feeds on small, bottom-dwelling invertebrates. Distribution includes the western Indian Ocean, Red Sea, eastwards to the Maldives, Mauritius, extending to southern KwaZulu-Natal. Relatively common.

BLUESPOTTED WRASSE – *Macropharyngodon cyanoguttatus*
Attains 11 cm. Initial phase individuals and terminal females have a dark brown, almost black body with a blue spot on each scale. The snout, nape and dorsal part of the head are yellow, and the reminder of the head is brownish yellow with irregular dark-edged blue bands. The rear half of the tail is white or translucent. Terminal males have a brownish-yellow body and tail, with a dark-edged blue spot on the scales. The head is dull orange-yellow with irregular dark blue lines forming a reticulated pattern. Occurs singly and in pairs, inhabiting mainly offshore coral and rocky reefs at depths of 12-40 m. Diet consists of bottom-dwelling invertebrates. Distribution includes Mauritius, Reunion and KwaZulu-Natal. Uncommon and similar in appearance to wrasses of the genus *Anampses,* which can cause confusion with identification.

MADAGASCAR WRASSE – *Macropharyngodon vivienae*
Attains 11 cm. Initial phase and terminal females are pale reddish with a red spot on each body scale. The head is covered with closely spaced, irregular yellow spotted lines. A thin red line occurs under the eye. The main distinguishing feature is the blue-edged black spot on the upper body behind the gill cover. A small black spot is also usually present at the rear of the dorsal fin. The basic body colour of the terminal male is similar, but the blue edging to the black spot breaks up and increases in area. Frequents offshore coral and rock reefs, ranging in depth from 12-30 m. Favours areas of mixed sand, rubble and corals. Occurs singly or in small groups and feeds on small bottom-dwelling invertebrates. Known from Madagascar and KwaZulu-Natal. A relatively uncommon species.

CHISELTOOTH WRASSE – *Pseudodax moluccanus*
Attains 25 cm. This robust wrasse has a grey ground colour with a reddish-brown spot on each body scale, and a wash of orange-red colour on the nape and the dorsal surface. The upper lip is yellow, with a blue streak above it crossing to the lower cheek. The tail fin is bluish black, with a pale yellow bar at the base. Both phases have the same basic coloration. Juveniles are black with two blue longitudinal stripes on upper and lower body respectively. Found on offshore coral reefs in various habitats ranging in depth from 3-40 m. Small juveniles are secretive and sometimes clean other fish. Adults feed on encrusting invertebrates, which are removed by using their strong chisel-like teeth. Widespread throughout Indo-Pacific, extending to KwaZulu-Natal. A relatively common species.

Bicolour cleaner wrasse

Divided wrasse (terminal male)

Divided wrasse (initial phase)

Bluespotted wrasse (initial phase)

Madagascar wrasse

Chiseltooth wrasse

SMALLTAIL WRASSE – *Pseudojuloides cerasinus*
Attains 12 cm. Initial phase and terminal females are rather inconspicuous due to their dull salmon-pink coloration and their pale yellow median fins. In contrast, the males are strikingly coloured with an olive-green body and a double mid-lateral stripe of blue (above) and yellow. The tail has a large blue-edged black bar on the fin. Generally swims close to the bottom over rocky and weedy areas. Females are sometimes found in groups and are more common than males. Inhabit offshore coral and rocky reefs to depths of 15-60 m. Diet consists of small, bottom-living invertebrates. Widespread throughout Indo-Pacific, extending to southern KwaZulu-Natal. A moderately common species.

CUTRIBBON WRASSE – *Stethojulis interrupta*
Attains 13 cm. The initial phase colour pattern is pinkish brown with a pale underside and a mid-lateral diffuse black stripe. A dark honeycomb pattern covers the belly and there is a greenish area to the rear of the pectoral fin. Terminal males are olive-grey on upper half of body and greenish below with a blue line along the back, adjacent to the dorsal fin, and another short mid-lateral blue line on rear half of body. There are also two blue to purplish short lines on the head, extending backwards from the snout above and below the eye. Found in most reef habitats as well as on seagrass beds. Ranges in depth from 4-25 m. Like other members of the genus *Stethojulis*, it feeds by sorting out small animals from mouthfuls of sand taken from the seabed. Widespread throughout Indo-West Pacific, Red Sea, south to the Eastern Cape. More abundant on shallower reefs. Similar in appearance to the bluelined wrasse, *Stethojulis albovittata*, and the three-ribbon wrasse, *Stethojulis strigiventer*.

REDCHEEK WRASSE (BLUENECK WRASSE) – *Thalassoma genivittatum*
Attains 20 cm. The colour pattern is similar between the phases of this species. Initial phase and terminal females have a bluish-green upper body and head, a pale underside and a prominent yellow area at the base of the tail. Irregular bluish lines extend over the cheeks. Terminal males are similar in colour, but have an additional yellow band across the body at the rear of the head. The tail and outer area of the pectoral fins are distinctly blue. Occasionally seen swimming in groups over inshore and offshore reefs at depths of 10-35 m. A very active wrasse, constantly on the move foraging for bottom-dwelling invertebrates. A limited distribution, only having been recorded from southern KwaZulu-Natal to southern Mozambique and Mauritius. An uncommon species.

SURGE WRASSE (RAINBOW WRASSE) – *Thalassoma purpureum*
Attains 43 cm. The colour pattern of this species is similar for all phases. Terminal males have three reddish-pink horizontal stripes on a green background, with numerous reddish-pink vertical lines between the stripes. Distinctive pinkish markings radiate from the eye. Juveniles, initial phase and terminal females have a more reticulated pattern and are pale green with reddish brown stripes and lines. Males tend to grow larger and are more brightly coloured than females. Occurs singly or in small groups. Found along rocky shores and on shallow inshore reefs, with juveniles often found in tidal pools. Rarely seen in depths over 10 m. Diet comprises mainly crabs, sea urchins, brittlestars and small fishes. Widespread throughout Indo-Pacific, Red Sea, south to the Eastern Cape. Juveniles and initial phase individuals are almost identical in colour pattern to the juvenile and initial phase ladder wrasse, *Thalassoma trilobatum*, which has a C-shaped line on the side of the snout in front of the eyes. A very common species. Adults are shy and are constantly on the move in the search for food.

Smalltail wrasse (terminal male)

Smalltail wrasse (initial phase)

Cutribbon wrasse (terminal male)

Cutribbon wrasse (initial phase)

Redcheek wrasse (terminal male)

Surge wrasse (terminal male)

LADDER WRASSE (CHRISTMAS WRASSE) – *Thalassomma trilobatum*
Attains 35 cm. The ladder wrasse is more robust than other *Thalassoma* species. Terminal males have an orange body with two ladder-like rows of blue-edged, green stripes along the sides. Juveniles, initial phase and terminal females are green with two pinkish-red stripes and numerous vertical lines, dividing the sides into a reticular pattern. Close-set maroon spots mark the dorsal surface and the upper head. An important diagnostic marking is the C-shaped line on the side of the snout in front of the eye. Frequents the surge zones of rocky shores and shallow reefs, seldom deeper than 15 m. Juveniles are often found in tidal pools. An active swimmer, constantly on the move and feeding on crustaceans, molluscs and brittle stars. Widespread throughout Indo-Pacific, south to the Eastern Cape. This very common wrasse is often mistaken for a parrotfish. The juvenile colour pattern is almost identical to that of the juvenile surge wrasse, *Thalassoma purpureum*, which lacks the C-shaped line on the snout.

SIXBAR WRASSE – *Thalassoma hardwicke*
Attains 20 cm. Identified by six slightly diagonal black saddles on the back, and reddish to pinkish broad lines radiating from the eyes. The body colour is pale green dorsally and bluish-white ventrally. Terminal males are more blue on the ventral surface. This species occurs in a variety of habitats, such as intertidal areas, tropical lagoons and offshore reefs to a depth of 15 m. Juveniles are secretive and inhabit weedy and seagrass areas. Feeds on bottom-living crustaceans, zooplankton and small fishes. Widespread throughout Indo-Pacific, extending south to northern KwaZulu-Natal. Rare in South African waters.

Parrotfishes – Family Scaridae
Parrotfishes are relatives of wrasses and are so named for their bright colours and their strong parrot-like beaks, which are used to scrape algae and polyps from coral and rocks. Like wrasses, most parrotfishes change colour with growth. Initial phase individuals consist of both males and females. Many species appear similar during the initail phase and are difficult to identify. They are also drab in colour whilst terminal males are more colourful. Females are able to change sex to become colourful terminal (sexually mature) males. Parrotfishes extract organic food matter from coral rock by crushing it with their unique grinding plates. Clouds of chalky residue are regularly excreted as these fish move about the reef, contributing substantially to the production of coral sand in tropical waters. At night, some species secrete an unappetising cocoon of mucus around themselves for protection while they are asleep in a crevice in the reef.

BRIDLED PARROTFISH – *Scarus frenatus*
Attains 47 cm. Terminal males are distinguished by a dark blue to green upper head, shading to a blue-green body, and then abruptly changing to pale blue or pale green at the rear of the body. There are also irregular pink markings on the throat. The initial phase colour is brownish-yellow to reddish-brown with six dark brown stripes along the sides and a broad pale band on the caudal peduncle. The fins are reddish to pink. Juveniles are found in areas of coral and rubble. Males are usually solitary and females often form small groups. Inhabits mainly offshore reef slopes and drop-offs at depths of 8-30 m. Feeds on algae and polyps. Widespread throughout Indo-Pacific, Red Sea, south to northern KwaZulu-Natal. Uncommon.

TRICOLOUR PARROTFISH – *Scarus tricolor*
Attains 40 cm. Terminal males are greenish with pink-edged scales and two long green stripes on the head, one above and the other below the eye. Usually these stripes are shorter in other similar species. The initial phase is dark purplish to black becoming paler on the underside with yellow anal, ventral and tail fins. Also has a yellow iris and a pale oval patch on the top of the head. Usually a solitary species, but occasionally observed in groups. This parrotfish frequents tropical lagoons and exposed outer slopes of coral reefs. Occurs at depths ranging from 10-40 m. Diet consists of algae and coral polyps. Known from the central Pacific to East Africa, extending south to northern KwaZulu-Natal. Relatively common.

FIVESADDLE PARROTFISH (DUSKY-CAPPED PARROTFISH) – *Scarus scaber*
Attains 37 cm. Initial and terminal male phases have distinctive colour patterns. The photograph shows an initial phase individual with a terminal male in the background. Terminal males are green with salmon-pink scale margins. Greyish blue from upper head to rear of pectoral fin. There is a broad band of blue-green from snout to pectoral fin. The throat area is salmon-pink. Initial phase individuals are pale yellow dorsally and pinkish-white on the lower sides, with four dark grey saddles on the back. Initial phase individuals often occur in small groups. A shallow-water species, favouring protected coral reefs and tropical lagoons in depths ranging from 1-20 m. Feeds on algae and coral polyps. Known from the islands of the western Indian Ocean, East Africa, extending to northern KwaZulu-Natal. Common.

Ladder wrasse (male)

Ladder wrasse (female)

Sixbar wrasse (initial phase)

Bridled parrotfish (terminal male)

Tricolour parrotfish (initial phase)

Fivesaddle parrotfish (initial phase)

BICOLOUR PARROTFISH – *Cetoscarus bicolor*
Attains 80 cm. Terminal males are bright green, with a pink margin to the scales, and pink spots on the upper head and front of the body. Initial phase colour is reddish-brown with a pale yellow back. Body scales are rimmed and spotted in black. Juveniles are white, with a prominent black-edged orange band across the head and a large black spot on dorsal fin. Frequents coral-rich areas of tropical lagoons and offshore reefs, ranging from the shallows to at least 30 m. Feeds on algae and coral polyps. Widespread throughout Indo-Pacific, Red Sea, south to central Mozambique. A relatively common species.

CHRISTMAS PARROTFISH (STAR-EYE PARROTFISH) – *Calotomus carolinus*
Attains 50 cm. Terminal males have a dusky blue-green and brownish-red coloration, with pink edges to the scales and pink lines radiating from the eyes. Initial phase individuals are mottled dark orange-brown with pale blotches shading to a pale orange underside. Occurs singly or in small groups. Inhabits tropical lagoons and offshore reefs to depths of 10-30 m. Feeds on algae and seagrass. Widespread throughout Indo-Pacific, extending to southern KwaZulu-Natal. A relatively common species.

LONGNOSE PARROTFISH – *Hipposcarus harid*
Attains 75 cm but 55 cm is more common. Recognized by the long shape of its snout and concave head profile. The initial phase colour is grey to light tan with a pinkish hue. Median fins are pale blue. Terminal males are pale green with scales lined with pink. A horizontal pink line occurs on the cheek and gill cover. The median fins are pink with a pale blue border. Males are usually solitary and females form small groups. Found in depths of 1-25 m. Feeds on algae and coral polyps. Distribution includes the western Indian Ocean, Red Sea, south to Bazaruto, Mozambique. A common species.

Barracudas – Family Sphyraenidae
Barracudas occur in all tropical and temperate seas, and include 20 known species. They are slender, silvery fishes with a forked tail and two widely spaced dorsal fins. The head is pointed with a protruding lower jaw. The mouth is large with long, knife-like teeth. They are voracious predators of other fishes and frequently occur in small to large shoals in open water. Only dangerous if provoked.

PICKHANDLE BARRACUDA (SEAPIKE) – *Sphyraena jello*
Attains 150 cm. Distinguished by its silvery body, which is yellow-green dorsally and white ventrally. The tail is yellow. About 20 dusky wavy crossbars, which extend to just below the lateral line are present along the body. Occurs singly, in small groups or in large shoals by day near coastal reefs. Feeds on reef fishes and squid at night. Widespread throughout western Pacific, Red Sea and East Africa extending south to Port Elizabeth. A moderately common species.

SAWTOOTH BARRACUDA (CHEVRON BARRACUDA) – *Sphyraena putnamiae*
Attains 90 cm. Identified by approximately 20 distinctive chevron-shaped dark bars along the sides of its silvery body. The tail fin is dusky with a black margin. Frequents coastal reefs where it forms large dense shoals during the day. Feeds at night mainly on reef fishes and squid. Ranges throughout tropical Indo-Pacific, Red Sea extending south to KwaZulu-Natal. A moderately common species.

Sandsmelts (sandperches) – Family Mugiloididae
Sandsmelts are a group of small elongate, cylindrical shaped fish with large mouths and thick lips. They live in sand and rubble areas near reefs. Characterized by the way they rest on the bottom, supporting themselves on their pelvic fins, ready to ambush prey. When threatened, they dash off and then come to an abrupt halt a short distance away. Their eyes are pronounced and orientated as much upwards as laterally. Can be confused with lizardfishes, but have a more pointed mouth, continuous dorsal and anal fins, and a square tail. They are territorial, and generally approachable underwater.

BLOTCHLIP SANDSMELT (YELLOWBAR SANDPERCH) – *Parapercis xanthozona*
Attains 25 cm. Distinguished by a whitish to light brown ground colour with numerous small orange-brown markings on the back and close-set irregular orange-brown spots on the head. Three dark brown blotches mark each side of the upper lip. Nine indistinct orange-brown crossbars occur on the sides with a white blotch in the middle of the tail fin. Generally found singly in the protected waters of bays, tropical lagoons and in sandy areas of offshore reefs in depths of 3-20 m. Feeds on small invertebrates and fishes. Ranges throughout Indo-West Pacific, south to KwaZulu-Natal. A relatively common species.

Bicolour parrotfish (terminal male)

Christmas parrotfish (terminal male)

Longnose parrotfish (terminal male)

Pickhandle barracuda

Sawtooth barracuda

Blotchlip sandsmelt

ROSY SANDSMELT (REDSPOTTED SANDPERCH) – *Parapercis schauinslandi*
Attains 14 cm. Has an overall orange-red coloration, white crossbars along the sides and two red spots at the base of the tail, one above the other. Frequents bays, harbours and offshore reefs, ranging in depth from 3-20 m. Favours open sand and rubble bottoms. Occurs singly. Diet comprises small invertebrates and fishes. Known from Hawaii, Seychelles, Comoros and central KwaZulu-Natal. Uncommon.

Blennies – Family Blenniidae

Blennies are a prolific family (over 300 species) of small elongated scaleless fish. They have a single continuous dorsal fin and are mostly bottom-dwelling fishes, ranging from the intertidal zone to offshore reefs. Due to their small size and cryptic coloration, many blennies go unnoticed. This family can be roughly divided into two main groups: sabretooth blennies, which are free-swimming, and combtooth blennies, which are bottom-dwelling. Bottom-dwelling blennies and gobies are similar in looks and habits (*see* p 92).

Sabretoothed blennies

This group of free-swimming, slender blennies are often boldly marked and have small downward-facing mouths. They are characterized by two sabre-like teeth in the lower jaw, used for defence and for biting the scales and skins from other fish for food. Active swimmers, that remain close to the reef, so when danger approaches, they can hastily retreat to a small hole or crevice into which they back tail first.

FLOATING BLENNY (LANCE BLENNY) – *Aspidontus dussumieri*
Attains 12 cm. Has a whitish body with a broad black stripe on the side, stretching from eye to tail. Stripe may have pale inter-spaces. Fins are pale yellow. Inhabits inshore reefs, favouring rocky and silty habitats in depths of 3-20 m. Empty tubeworms often provide it with shelter. Feeds off fish and on algae and detritus. Widespread throughout Indo-Pacific, Red Sea, extending to the southern Eastern Cape. Common.

TWOSTRIPE BLENNY (SABRETOOTH FANG BLENNY) *Plagiotremus rhinorhynchos*
Attains 12 cm. Has two distinct colour phases, either dark brown to black with a blue stripe along the back from snout to tail, or orange with two narrow blue lines from snout to tail. Inhabits inshore and offshore reefs at depths of 1-40 m. Mimics the cleaner wrasse, *Labroides dimidiatus*, by pretending to remove parasites and mucus off other fish, but instead feeds on them by taking bites out of their flesh and beating a hasty retreat. Widespread throughout Indo-Pacific, south to the Eastern Cape. A common species.

Combtooth blennies

This group of bottom-dwelling blennies are characterized by high-set eyes, blunt heads and wide mouths with comb-like teeth specially adapted for scraping algae off rocks. Many have tentacles (cirri) above the eyes and some have fleshy crests on the head. Many similar species make identification difficult. Species from the intertidal zone are able to 'hop' from pool to pool in search of food. Hence the common name rockskipper.

BLACKFLAP BLENNY (EARED OR EARSPOT BLENNY) – *Cirripectes auritus*
Attains 9 cm. Recognized by the yellow-edged dark blue spot on the upper gill cover. The rear two-thirds of body is uniformly pale with numerous scattered, fine, dusky spots. The head and front third of the body are light brown. Inhabits shallow coral reefs to a depth of 20 m. Feeds on algae. Widespread throughout Indo-Pacific, extending south to northern KwaZulu-Natal. A relatively common species.

REDSTREAKED BLENNY (SCARLET-SPOTTED BLENNY) *Cirripectes stigmaticus*
Attains 12 cm. Males are dark brown, with a scarlet honeycombed pattern on the head, which breaks into irregular bright scarlet spots and short lines on the body. Females are dull olive with a rust-coloured honeycombed pattern on head, which breaks up into irregular spots on the body. Frequents exposed coral reefs to a depth of 20 m. Tends to perch on coral heads. Feeds on algae. Widespread throughout Indo-Pacific, extending down the east African coast to northern KwaZulu-Natal. Uncommon.

GOLDEN BLENNY (MIDAS BLENNY) – *Ecsenius midas*
Attains 13 cm. Colour is orange-yellow overall. Has two short diagonal blue lines located on the top and bottom of each eye. The dorsal fin has a blue margin. Found on rocky and coral reefs in depths of 2-30 m. Shelters in small holes in the reef, often seen with just the head protruding. Different to most other combtooth blennies in that it is free-swimming and feeds on zooplankton. Occurs throughout Indo-Pacific, extending to southern KwaZulu-Natal. A common species that is often encountered swimming with sea goldies.

Rosy sandsmelt

Floating blenny

Twostripe blenny

Blackflap blenny

Redstreaked blenny

Golden blenny

NALOLO BLENNY – *Ecsenius nalolo*

Attains 5 cm. This small, light brown blenny has whitish spots scattered over the rear half of the body. A distinctive horizontal dashed brown line extends backwards from the eye. Tiny brown spots are also sprinkled over the gill covers. Inhabits inshore and offshore reefs. Often found perching on coral heads. Found in depths from 3-20 m. Feeds on algae and small invertebrates. Ranges from the Red Sea, Maldives and the western Indian Ocean, extending south to KwaZulu-Natal. An uncommon species.

RIPPLED ROCKSKIPPER – *Istiblennius edentulus*

Attains 16 cm. Males are greenish grey with reddish-brown vertical bars along body and a fleshy crest on the head. Bars may occur in pairs. Females lack the crest and the posterior bars become broken and change to spots. Both sexes can 'turn-on' one or two horizontal pale stripes on the head. Frequents rocky shores, mangroves and harbour habitats. Rarely seen deeper than 1 m. Feeds on algae. Widely distributed throughout Indo-Pacific, Red Sea, south to the Eastern Cape. A very common species.

MANED BLENNY – *Scartella emarginata*

Attains 10 cm. Body is light brown with five to six vertical dusky bands on the sides and fine dark brown spots scattered over body and median fins. A mane-like row of tentacles occurs on top of the head. Short tentacles are located next to each eye. Feeds on small invertebrates and algae. Distributed throughout the Atlantic and the Indian Ocean, ranging from southern Angola to India. Very common in tidal pools.

Klipfishes – Family Clinidae

All 40 species of klipfish that occur in southern Africa are endemic to the region. They are moderately small fishes with elongated, scaled bodies compressed posteriorly. Characterized by a long dorsal fin with well developed spines, extending from the head to the base of the tail. These camouflaged fishes are more common in cooler temperate waters. They frequent kelp beds, weedy areas of rocky shores and tidal pools.

SUPER KLIPFISH – *Clinus superciliosus*

Attains 30 cm. The colour pattern is extremely variable and may be plain dark green, red, brown or yellowish-green, with a solid or broken white longitudinal stripe along its side, tapering towards the tail. Another variation has six vertical bars with a multi-coloured mottled pattern. The adopted colour pattern depends on habitat. The main diagnostic features are the extended first three dorsal spines that form a crest, and the distinctive notch between the third and fourth dorsal spines. Found lying on rocky and weedy bottoms in tidal pools, along rocky shores, harbours and offshore reefs to a depth of at least 30 m. Preys on small invertebrates. Ranges from southern Namibia to southern Eastern Cape. A very common species.

SPECKLED KLIPFISH – *Clinus venustris*

Attains 12 cm. This klipfish has a variable colour pattern, but is usually mottled reddish brown with several dark brown bands along the body. May also have a dark-edged, white inclined bar on the cheek, but sometimes the bar is replaced by dark speckles. The main diagnostic feature is its colourful eyes, which have a light green iris rimmed by a broken orange line. Two black spots mark the unnotched dorsal fin. Inhabits tidal pools and rocky shores in depths from 0,3-30 m. Feeds on small invertebrates. Ranges from Luderitz in Namibia to Port Alfred in the Eastern Cape. A common species.

Gobies – Family Gobiidae

Gobies constitute the largest single family of marine fish. They have small slender bodies and many are inconspicuous. Gobies and blennies are often mistaken for each other, but can be distinguished by their dorsal fins. Gobies have two separate fins, while blennies have a single, continuous fin. Most gobies have scales, while blennies are scaleless. Bottom-living gobies tend to rest in a stiff, straight position, while blennies are more flexed and curved. Gobies are mostly bottom-living but some species are free-swimming. Bottom-dwelling species rest on their pectoral and pelvic fins. They can form a small suction disc between the pelvic fins to anchor themselves on the substrate during surge or current. Their habitats include estuaries, mangroves, rocky shores and offshore reefs. Diet varies according to species.

INNER-SPOT GOBY – *Fusigobius inframaculatus*

Attains 8 cm. This goby has long first dorsal fin rays and orange spots scattered over a pale head and body. A dark blotch marks the base of the tail. Occurs singly. Frequents offshore reefs, found lying on the sand beneath overhangs at depths of 9-20 m. Feeds on small invertebrates. Distribution includes Mauritius, Seychelles and the East African coast extending to southern KwaZulu-Natal. A common species.

Nalolo blenny

Rippled rockskipper (male and female)

Maned blenny

Super klipfish

Speckled klipfish

Inner-spot goby

DECORATED GOBY – *Istigobius decoratus*
Attains 12 cm. Best recognized by its pale to yellowish body with a brown honeycombed pattern along the upper sides. Has two horizontal rows of rectangular dark brown spots along the lower side and strongly spotted dorsal, caudal and anal fins. Lives on sandy and silty bottoms and shelters under rocks or in caves. Found in most sand and rubble habitats on coral and rocky reefs, ranging in depth from 1-18 m. Diet comprises small invertebrates. Widespread throughout Indo-Pacific, Red Sea, south to Mozambique, extending to KwaZulu-Natal. A very common species.

WHITE-BARRED REEF GOBY – *Amblygobius semicinctus*
Attains 10 cm. A burrow-dwelling species, identified by several narrow vertical white bars on the lower half of darkish body and dark-edged orange spots on the head. Highly variable in colour, depending on habitat. The rays of the first dorsal fin are extended above the second dorsal fin. Usually found in pairs. Inhabits shallow reefs and tropical lagoons, especially sand and rubble areas, seagrass beds and harbours. Hovers just above the bottom and never strays far from its borrow. Occurs in depths from 1-22 m. Feeds on algae and tiny invertebrates by sifting mouthfuls of sand through its gills. Ranges from East Africa, south to Mozambique and east to Indonesia. A relatively common species.

RAILWAY GLIDER (TWO STRIPE OR BLACKLINED SLEEPER GOBY) – *Valenciennea helsdingenii*
Attains 16 cm. Identified by its brown dorsal surface, whitish sides and two brown to orange stripes along the body, extending from the snout to the tail. A prominent black spot edged in white occurs on the first dorsal fin. Usually encountered in pairs and never strays far from its burrow. Occurs on inshore and offshore coral and rocky reefs in depths of 5-45 m, favouring a mixed sand and rubble habitat. Sifts mouthfuls of sand through its gills for small invertebrates and algae. Widespread throughout tropical Indo-Pacific, extending to southern KwaZulu-Natal. An uncommon species.

BLUESPOTTED SLEEPER GOBY (SIX-SPOT GOBY) – *Valenciennea sexguttata*
Attains 13 cm. This goby has a whitish body and pale blue spots on the cheeks. The dorsal fin has a small black tip. Adults usually occur in pairs, juveniles may form small groups. Typically builds a burrow in the sand next to a rock. Inhabits sheltered bays or tropical lagoons with silty or sandy bottoms where it is rarely found deeper than 10 m. Feeds on small invertebrates and algae by filtering mouthfuls of sand through its gills. Distributed throughout tropical Indo-Pacific, south to Bazaruto, Mozambique. Reasonably common.

STEINITZ'S SHRIMP GOBY – *Amblyeleotris steinitzi*
Attains 8 cm. Belongs to a group known as shrimp or prawn gobies. There are several similar species, which makes identification difficult. They have a symbiotic relationship with snapping prawns, *Alpheus* sp. and live together in a sand burrow constructed and maintained by the prawn, whilst the goby acts as a lookout, so protecting the prawn. The Steinitz's shrimp goby is recognized by the five reddish-brown bands along a whitish body and two spots above each eye. The bands are pale in some individuals. The snout and area around the eyes is often dusky brown, but dark in the Red Sea species. Nearly always found in pairs, but the female is often in the burrow and is rarely seen. Inhabits sandy areas of tropical lagoons and off-shore reefs, in depths ranging from 6-27 m. Feeds on small invertebrates and zooplankton. Widespread throughout Indo-Pacific, Red Sea, south to KwaZulu-Natal. An uncommon species.

SEAWHIP GOBY – *Bryaninops yongei*
Attains 4 cm. Members of this genus are very specialized in their habitat. They live and lay their eggs on seawhips, gorgonians and certain species of *Acropora* corals. Each species associates itself with a particular host, which it only leaves to capture passing food. The seawhip goby is transparent, with a white dashed line and about six reddish-brown bars or blotches along the body. Usually found in pairs, in association with black corals (family Antipathidae), in particular the straight stemmed variety of the genus *Cirrhipathes*, which grow in areas of exposed current at depths of 15-60 m. Feeds on zooplanton. Common throughout Indo-Pacific, extending to southern KwaZulu-Natal. These tiny, well camouflaged gobies are only noticed by those purposely looking for them.

Dartfishes (dart gobies) – Family Microdesmidae
Dartfishes were previously included in the family Gobiidae (gobies), but now are recognized as a subfamily of Microdesmidae (wormfishes) called Ptereleotrinae. Dartfishes are small slender fishes with oblique mouths. Most have divided dorsal fins. Normally found in areas of moderate current, swimming a metre or so above the bottom. They shelter in the reef or in sand burrows and dart into their shelter when danger approaches.

Decorated goby

White-barred reef goby

Railway glider

Bluespotted sleeper goby

Steinitz's shrimp goby

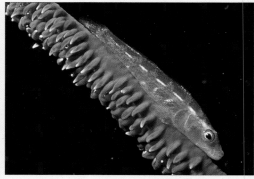

Seawhip goby

ZEBRA GOBY (ZEBRA DARTFISH) – *Ptereleotris zebra*

Attains 11 cm. Identified by its greenish-grey ground colour with numerous narrow pink crossbars fringed with blue along the body. Also has a purplish area below the eye and on gill cover and a dark blue margin on both dorsal fins. Usually found in aggregations on shallow coral reefs exposed to surge in depths of 2-12 m. Males tend to lower and spread their pelvic fins, beating them rapidly during courtship displays as shown in the photograph. When seeking refuge, a number of these fish are seen to dart into the same hole. Diet consists mainly of zooplankton. Widespread throughout Indo-Pacific, Red Sea, south to northern KwaZulu-Natal. This generally uncommon species is shy and difficult to approach.

BLACKTAIL GOBY (SPOT-TAIL GOBY) – *Ptereleotris heteroptera*

Attains 12 cm. Recognized by its slender pale bluish-grey body and black spot on its yellow tail. Also has a prominent iridescent blue eye ring. Favours sand and rubble bottoms of tropical lagoons, bays and exposed coral reefs in depths ranging from 7-46 m. Adults are usually found in pairs whilst juveniles occur in small groups. They tend to hover just above the bottom near their burrow. Feeds on zooplankton. Occurs throughout Indo-Pacific, Red Sea, extending south to northern KwaZulu-Natal. A relatively common but very shy fish, which quickly retreats into its burrow if approached.

Surgeonfishes – Family Acanthuridae

Surgeonfishes are exquisitely patterned and colourful reef fishes. They are small to medium-sized, oval-shaped and laterally compressed fishes with high-set eyes and small mouths. Species of the subfamily Acanthurinae have a scalpel-like spine that folds forward into a groove (sheath) on either side of the base of the tail. These sharp spines give the family its common name. The spines are used for defence. Surgeonfishes are a very important group of herbivores as they help control the growth of algae on reefs. Some deep-water shoaling species feed primarily on zooplankton. Surgeonfishes of the genus *Zebrasoma* are often referred to as tangs. Unicornfishes (subfamily Nasinae) have a more elongated body and some develop a horn-like protrusion on the forehead. They also feature a pair of hook-like, bony keel plates at the base of the tail.

CHOCOLATE SURGEON (THOMPSON'S SURGEONFISH) – *Acanthurus thompsoni*

Attains 27 cm. Capable of rapidly changing colour from light bluish-grey to dark brown. Has a white tail, and black spot at the rear of the dorsal fin base. Juveniles have pale yellow fins. Occurs on most offshore coral reefs in depths of 4-17 m, where it is often encountered in loose groups. Feeds on zooplankton above reefs. Widespread throughout Indo-Pacific, south to northern KwaZulu-Natal. A common species.

YELLOWFIN SURGEON – *Acanthurus xanthopterus*

Attains 62 cm. Overall colour is purplish grey to brown, but can change abruptly to light blue-grey with a pattern of irregular horizontal brown to dark grey lines on the sides of the body. Has a distinctive yellow eye blotch, yellow pectoral fins, a bluish tail with a whitish band at the base and a black spine sheath. Adults usually occur in small to large groups preferring deep offshore reefs down to a depth of 90 m. Juveniles live in shallow protected areas. Grazes the surface of sand and rubble for soft algae. Distributed throughout Indian Ocean and tropical eastern Pacific, south to KwaZulu-Natal. A common species, similar in colour to the pencilled surgeonfish, *Acanthurus dussumieri*, which has a white spine sheath and a spotted tail with a yellow band across the base.

STRIPED BRISTLETOOTH (LINED BRISTLETOOTH) – *Ctenochaetus striatus*

Attains 26 cm. The body is mostly dark brown with numerous inconspicuous thin blue longitudinal lines on the sides and small orange spots on the upper head. The soft portions of the dorsal and anal fins have dark horizontal lines The pectoral fins are usually yellow and a small black spot may be present at the rear base of the dorsal fin. Inhabits rocky shores, tropical lagoons and offshore reefs, in depths of 1-30 m, where it occurs singly or in small to large groups. Grazes on soft algae growing on reefs. Widespread throughout Indo-Pacific, south to KwaZulu-Natal. A very common surgeonfish.

PALETTE SURGEONFISH (BLUE TANG) – *Paracanthurus hepatus*

Attains 26 cm. Juveniles are a brilliant blue with a distinctive black pattern on the upper sides and a prominent yellow tail edged in black. Adults are similar in colour, but the lower sides change to a pale yellow. Frequents offshore reefs, ranging in depth from 5-40 m. Generally forms loose aggregations that swim 1-3 m above the reef. Juveniles shelter in groups among branching coral heads or in crevices in the reef. Feeds on zooplankton. Widespread throughout Indo-Pacific, extending to northern KwaZulu-Natal. Uncommon in South African waters. A very popular fish with marine aquarists.

Zebra goby

Blacktail goby

Chocolate surgeon

Yellowfin surgeon

Striped bristletooth

Palette surgeonfish

SPOTTED TANG (GEM SURGEONFISH OR MAURITIUS TANG) – *Zebrasoma gemmatum*

Attains 22 cm. This distinctive species has close-set white spots scattered over a dark brown to greenish-brown body and fins, and a prominent yellow tail. Members of the genus *Zebrasoma* are distinct from other surgeonfish species by their large dorsal and anal fins. This feature is proportionally larger in juveniles. Generally occurs singly on offshore coral and rocky reefs at depths of 10-60 m. Feeds on algae, which is grazed from rocks and dead coral. Distribution is confined to Mauritius, Madagascar and the east coast of southern Africa. A generally uncommon species that stays close to the reef.

BLACKTONGUE UNICORNFISH (SLEEK UNICORNFISH) – *Naso hexacanthus*

Attains 75 cm but 50 cm is more common. The colour of this sleek unicornfish is brown to bluish grey on the upper body, shading to a pale yellow on the lower sides. Capable of changing rapidly to pale blue. Other features include a blue tail and black lines on the cheek, extending to the gill cover. This species lacks a horn-like protrusion on the forehead. Generally occurs in shoals in mid-water near steep outer reef slopes. Sleeps in crevices in the reef at night. Ranges in depth from 6-135 m. Feeds on zooplankton. Widespread throughout Indo-Pacific, Red Sea, south to KwaZulu-Natal. A relatively common species.

SPOTTED UNICORNFISH – *Naso brevirostris*

Attains 60 cm. The adult spotted unicornfish has a well developed horn protruding from the forehead. The body coloration is olive-brown to grey with vertical dark lines on the sides of the body. The tail fin is whitish with a large dusky spot at the base. Often exhibits a broad bluish-white band across the front half of the body. This may become paler during behavioural displays with members of the species. Sub-adults have small dark spots on head and body. Frequents offshore reefs particularly along upper slopes and drop-offs. Ranges in depth from 4-45 m. Occurs singly or in small loose groups. Juveniles forage for algae on reefs and adults feed on zooplankton in mid-water. Common throughout Indo-Pacific, Red Sea, extending to southern KwaZulu-Natal.

BLUESPINE UNICORNFISH (SHORTNOSE UNICORNFISH) – *Naso unicornis*

Attains 70 cm. Adults develop a short bony horn on the forehead, which seldom extends beyond the front of the mouth. Juveniles lack a bony horn. The overall coloration is grey to light olive with a distinctive blue keel at the base of the tail. Long filaments on the tail often develop in adults. Encountered singly or in small groups on shallow to moderately deep reefs, ranging in depth from 1-40 m. Grazes on leafy algae for food. Widespread throughout Indo-Pacific, extending to southern KwaZulu-Natal. This common species is generally rather timid and difficult to approach closely.

BIGNOSE UNICORNFISH – *Naso vlamingii*

Attains 55 cm. Mature adults develop a large distinctive nose instead of a horn, and long tail filaments. Overall colour is yellowish brown with irregular vertical blue lines on sides and small blue spots on the head and back. A blue stripe runs from the eye to snout, and the lips are blue. A blue line extends along the base of both dorsal and anal fins. Capable of instantly 'turning' on or off its blue markings. Males are particularly colourful during courtship displays. Sleeps in a cave or crevice in the reef at night. Usually encountered in small loose groups on inshore and offshore reefs in open water at depths of 4-50 m. Feeds on zooplankton. Widespread throughout Indo-Pacific, possibly south to northern KwaZulu-Natal. Common in tropical regions.

Rabbitfishes – Family Siganidae

Rabbitfishes are closely related to surgeonfishes. Their bodies are elongate and compressed, exhibiting an evenly rounded profile. All rabbitfishes are herbivorous and have a small mouth with close set teeth, which are well suited to grazing algae. The fin spines are venomous and wounds from these spines are extremely painful. Some species occur in shoals, others in pairs. They are an important food source in some regions.

STARSPOTTED RABBITFISH (STARRY OR STELLATE RABBITFISH) – *Siganus stellatus*

Attains 40 cm. The starspotted rabbitfish has dark brown to black close-set spots scattered over a pale coloured head, body and tail. In the Red Sea, individuals have a yellow marking on the nape and upper back and yellow areas on the fins. This colouring is absent on individuals outside the Red Sea. Inhabits coral reefs and tropical lagoons to depths ranging from 3-45 m. Adults always occur in pairs and juveniles often in shoals. Sometimes enters estuaries to graze on algae in weedy areas. Widespread throughout the west and central Indian Ocean, Red Sea, extending to southern Mozambique. Relatively common.

Spotted tang

Blacktongue unicornfish

Spotted unicornfish

Bluespine unicornfish

Bignose unicornfish

Starspotted rabbitfish

DUSKY RABBITFISH (SQUARETAIL RABBITFISH) – *Siganus luridus*
Attains 30 cm. Coloration is usually yellowish brown, with a pale underside. Small blue spots occur on the sides of the body and there are several horizontal blue lines on the cheek. The yellowish tail has dusky vertical lines. Capable of dramatically changing colour to a dark yellowish-brown dorsally, and greyish on lower sides with a yellow stripe along the upper side and a white mid-lateral stripe. Occurs in pairs or small groups, inhabiting inshore and offshore reefs to a depth of 40 m. Feeds on algae. Ranges from the Red Sea to Reunion and Mauritius and recently also to southern KwaZulu-Natal. An uncommon species.

Tuna and mackerels – Family Scombridae

Members of this family are migratory. They are powerful, streamlined fishes, characterized by a pointed snout, slender caudal peduncle with at least two small keels on each side and a deeply forked tail. These medium to large pelagic predators are extremely fast swimmers and are able to fold their dorsal fins back into a groove to improve their streamlining. Some species visit reefs while others remain in open water. Certain smaller species strain zooplankton through their gill rakers. Most hunt other fishes and pelagic invertebrates such as squid. They are among the most important of commercial and recreational sport fishes.

EASTERN LITTLE TUNA (MACKEREL TUNA) – *Euthynnus affinis*
Can attain 100 cm but 50 cm is more common. This medium-sized tuna has a robust spindle-shaped body with a greenish dorsal surface and blue wavy lines across its back. The lower sides and belly are silvery-grey. Several dark spots are usually present on the chest below the pectoral fin. Forms large, fast moving shoals in coastal waters and is often seen swimming over offshore reefs. Ranges in depth from 1-50 m. Preys on small fishes and is preyed upon by larger billfish. Widespread throughout tropical Indo-West Pacific, Red Sea, south to the Eastern Cape. Particularly abundant along the East Coast of southern Africa during summer months. Juveniles are often used as live bait to catch billfish.

MACKEREL (SLIMY OR CHUB MACKEREL) – *Scomber japonicus*
Attains 70 cm but 35 cm is more common. Has a slender, rounded body with a pointed snout and a narrow caudal peduncle. The upper body and head is a metallic green colour overlaid with dark oblique zig-zag lines. The lower sides and belly are silvery-white, sometimes with dark spots. The fins are yellowish to translucent. Usually observed in large shoals around pinnacles and shipwrecks. A pelagic fish ranging from surface waters to depths of 200 m. Feeds on zooplankton and small fish. Favours cooler, temperate waters and occurs in all oceans of the world, found locally from Namibia to Mozambique, and migrating to tropical waters during winter. An important food source for larger fishes and mammals.

Triggerfishes – Family Balistidae

Robust and laterally compressed fishes with oval-shaped bodies and high-set eyes. First dorsal spine can be locked in an erect position by the smaller trigger-like second spine. They swim by undulating the soft dorsal and anal fins, using the tail only when speed is required. When threatened, they seek refuge in a hole or crevice in the reef, firmly wedging themselves by erecting and locking the dorsal spine. Strong sharp teeth are used for crushing shellfish, crustaceans and sea urchins. Female triggerfish lay their eggs on the seabed, and defend them aggressively. Some species make their nest by digging a shallow crater in sand.

ORANGESTRIPPED TRIGGERFISH – *Balistapus undulatus*
Attains 30 cm. Has an overall green colour with distinctive yellow to orange diagonal stripes on head and body. Adult males lack stripes on top of snout. Usually occurs singly and is found in various reef habitats to a depth of 50 m. Feeds on a wide variety of food such as sea urchins, crabs, fishes, molluscs, worms and sponges. Widespread throughout Indo-West Pacific, Red Sea, extending to southern KwaZulu-Natal. This common triggerfish is timid, seeking refuge in a crevice when threatened.

TITAN TRIGGERFISH (GIANT, DOTTY OR MOUSTACHE TRIGGERFISH) – *Balistoides viridescens*
Attains 75 cm. Recognized by its plump, oval-shaped body and yellowish coloration, which becomes paler towards the tail. Dark brown marks are found on each scale. Has a broad blackish zone extending from nape to pectoral base and a dark moustache above the mouth. Mouth bears large incisors. Adults occur singly or in pairs. Inhabits tropical lagoons and offshore reefs to a depth of 40 m. Diet consists of live corals, hard-bodied bottom-dwelling invertebrates and algae. Also known to eat the crown-of-thorns starfish. Found throughout Indo-West Pacific, Red Sea, extending to southern KwaZulu-Natal. A relatively common species, that is normally wary, but can be aggressive when guarding a nest. May attack unprovoked by charging at speed and ramming its victim or by biting. A potentially dangerous fish.

Dusky rabbitfish (plain form)

Dusky rabbitfish (striped form)

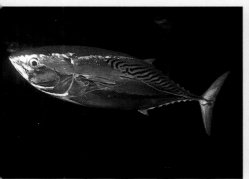

Eastern little tuna

Mackerel

Orangestriped triggerfish

Titan triggerfish

INDIAN TRIGGERFISH – *Melichthys indicus*

Attains 30 cm. This active triggerfish appears almost black from a distance except for the white lines at the base of both the second dorsal and the anal fins and the white margin on the rounded tail fin. However when viewed more closely, it has a number of indistinct longitudinal white lines formed by small spots on the rear half of the body. Often has a pale yellowish area between the first and second dorsal fins. Inhabits offshore reefs, where it occurs singly, but may form small loose groups when feeding on zooplankton above the reef. Ranges in depth from 10-30 m. Diet also includes algae, sponges and invertebrates. Widespread throughout the tropical Indian Ocean and Red Sea, extending to southern KwaZulu-Natal. A common species, similar to the black triggerfish, *Melichthys niger,* which has a concave tail and a vertical white line across the tail fin instead of a white margin.

RIPPLED TRIGGERFISH (BLUE OR YELLOW-SPOTTED TRIGGERFISH) – *Pseudobalistes fuscus*

Attains 55 cm. The rippled triggerfish changes its colour pattern quite dramatically with growth. Adults are deep blue to greyish-blue in colour with closely spaced yellowish spots, which may be joined to form irregular lines extending over the entire body. With growth, the tail fin develops long filaments. Juveniles are yellowish-brown and covered with numerous irregular bluish lines. This rather shy triggerfish inhabits offshore coral and rocky reefs, with juveniles occurring along rocky shores. Ranges in depth from1-50 m. Feeds on algae, invertebrates and small fishes. Widespread throughout Indo-West Pacific, Red Sea, extending to southern KwaZulu-Natal. An uncommon species in South African waters.

RECTANGULAR TRIGGERFISH (WEDGE-TAIL OR PATCHY TRIGGERFISH)
– *Rhinecanthus rectangulus*

Attains 25 cm. The distinctive markings of this triggerfish make it easy to recognize. A broad black band extends diagonally across the body from eye to anal fin, separating the brown upper side from the head and pale chest. The caudal peduncle has a wedge-shaped black marking, lined with a pale greenish-gold, which is preceded by a similarly coloured parallel line. It also has a blue band across the upper snout. A territorial species that never strays far from its shelter. Inhabits rocky shores and shallow reefs exposed to surge. Rarely seen deeper than 10 m. Juveniles are sometimes found in tidal pools. Feeds on algae, detritus, and a variety of small bottom-dwelling animals. Wary, quickly swimming away or diving into a hole if approached too closely. Occurs throughout Indo-West Pacific, Red Sea, south to the Eastern Cape. A common species.

GILDED TRIGGERFISH – *Xanthichthys auromarginatus*

Attains 25 cm. This relatively small, striking triggerfish has an oval shaped head profile, which is typical of the genus *Xanthichthys*. Females are grey overall with a series of small white spots along the scale rows. A black line extends along the base of both the second dorsal and anal fins, and the tail fin has a black border around it. Males have a lighter grey to brownish-grey body with a large bright blue patch on the lower head, and the median fins have distinctive yellow margins. Inhabits moderately deep offshore reefs in depths of 20-70 m. Rarely encountered in less than 30 m. Lives singly or in loose groups of mixed sexes in areas with moderate currents. Feeds on zooplankton in mid-water above reefs. Recorded from isolated localities in the Indo-Pacific. Known to occur in South African waters along the KwaZulu-Natal coast from Sodwana Bay to Protea Banks. A rare species.

Indian triggerfish

Rippled triggerfish

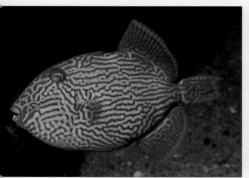

Rippled triggerfish (juvenile)

Rectangular triggerfish

Gilded triggerfish (male)

Gilded triggerfish (female)

STRIPED TRIGGERFISH (LINED TRIGGERFISH) – *Xanthichthys lineopunctatus*
Attains 30 cm. This species has a deep rounded chest profile and a pale grey body with dark horizontal lines on the upper sides and spots on lower sides. The head is brownish-grey, with at least three horizontal blue to brown lines on the cheeks. The second dorsal and anal fins have a black line along both fin bases. The tail has a prominent reddish-brown border around it. Found on offshore reefs in depths of 20-60 m. Feeds on zooplankton above the reef. Known from the western Indian Ocean, Reunion and Japan. Rarely encountered in South African waters. An uncommon species.

Filefishes (leatherjackets) – Family Monacanthidae

Filefishes are closely related to triggerfishes. They have oval to elongated, laterally compressed bodies, and small mouths with protruding lips. They have a prominent first dorsal spine, which can be locked into a vertical position by a much smaller second spine. The scales are also small and coarse, giving the skin a file-like texture. Most species are able to change colour to match their surroundings. Some species are secretive. Most are omnivorous.

SCRIBBLED FILEFISH (SCRIBBLED LEATHERJACKET) – *Aluteres scriptus*
Attains 100 cm. This large filefish has an elongated body and a long broom-like tail. Its background colour varies, from pale grey or tan, to dark olive-brown, depending on the surroundings. Irregular blue spots, short lines and small black spots also cover the head and body. Adults frequent tropical lagoons and offshore coral reefs, in depths of 2-80 m. Often swims along at odd angles. Feeds on a wide variety of plants and bottom-dwelling animals. Distribution is worldwide in all tropical and subtropical seas, extending to the southern Eastern Cape. A shy solitary species, uncommon in most areas.

BLACKSADDLE MIMIC (MIMIC FILEFISH) – *Paraluteres prionurus*
Attains 10 cm. This small filefish has four distinct saddle-shaped black areas on a whitish body and a yellow tail. A blackish reticulated pattern is usually present on the sides. Usually solitary, it frequents tropical lagoons and offshore reefs to depths of 1-25 m. Feeds on bottom-dwelling invertebrates. Occurs throughout tropical Indo-West Pacific, extending to southern KwaZulu-Natal. An uncommon species that is almost identical in appearance to the poisonous model toby, *Canthigaster valentini*, which it mimics and often associates with for possible protection. The latter has dark spots on the sides, instead of a reticulated pattern, lacks the elongated first dorsal spine and has shorter dorsal and anal fin bases.

BARRED FILEFISH (WHITE SPOTTED OR YELLOW EYE LEATHERJACKET)
– *Cantherhines dumerilii*
Attains 35 cm. Has an oval-shaped body and uniform greyish-brown colour, often with a series of incomplete, darker vertical bars on the rear half of the body. Other features include whitish lips, a yellowish tail and a yellow iris. Also has two pairs of forward curved spines on caudal peduncle. Juveniles and sub-adults have white spots scattered over the body. Adults are usually encountered in pairs. Inhabits coral and rocky reefs, ranging in depth from 1-35 m. Feeds mainly on tips of branching corals, algae, sponges and various bottom-dwelling invertebrates. Widespread throughout tropical Indo-Pacific, south to the Eastern Cape. An uncommon and shy species.

REDTAIL FILEFISH (BLACKBAR OR EAR-SPOT FILEFISH) – *Pervagor janthinosoma*
Attains 14 cm. Best recognized by its orange-red tail fin with rows of small dark spots, and a dark blotch on the gill cover. The front half of the body is usually dark bluish and the rear half is greenish brown. Territorial and usually hides among branching corals. Occurs singly or in pairs. Inhabits offshore coral and rocky reefs and tropical lagoons, in depths of 2-20 m. Diet consists of algae and various small invertebrates. Widespread throughout Indo-West Pacific, extending to southern KwaZulu-Natal. Juveniles may reach the Eastern Cape. A moderately uncommon and secretive species.

LONGNOSE FILEFISH (HARLEQUIN FILEFISH) – *Oxymoncanthus longirostris*
Attains 10 cm. This small filefish has an elongated body with a long pointed snout and a small upturned mouth. Its green body is covered with numerous dark-edged orange spots, and orange stripes mark the snout. It also has a black blotch on the tail fin. Juveniles often form small groups and adults usually occur in pairs. Inhabits shallow reefs and tropical lagoons with rich coral growth in depths of 1-30 m. Found in thickets of *Acropora* coral and feeds exclusively on the polyps. Uses its pointed snout to snip the polyps from their skeletal cup. Distributed throughout the tropical Indo-West Pacific, extending to southern Mozambique. A moderately common species.

Striped triggerfish

Scribbled filefish

Blacksaddle mimic

Barred filefish

Redtail filefish

Longnose filefish

Boxfishes – Family Ostraciidae

Boxfishes are close relatives of blaasops (puffers) and porcupinefishes, and are so named because head and body are encased in hexagonal bony plates, fused into a rigid, box-like protective case. They lack pelvic fins. Generally brightly coloured and patterned. Markings often vary with age and sex. Sluggish yet manoeuvrable fish, that are able to secrete a poisonous mucus from the skin for protection against predators.

BOXY (YELLOW OR CUBE BOXFISH) – *Ostracion cubicus*

Attains 45 cm. Juveniles have a brilliant yellow, cube-shaped body, covered with tiny black spots. Adult females are bluish-grey, with blue fins and numerous black-edged, white to pale blue spots on carapace. Tiny dark spots also cover the body and fins. Adult males vary from yellowish green, ochre to purplish brown with round black-edged blue spots on the carapace. Inhabits inshore and offshore reefs. Generally solitary, usually seeking shelter under reef overhangs. Ranges in depth from 1-30 m. Feeds on algae, sponges and invertebrates. Widespread throughout Indo-West Pacific, Red Sea, south to the Eastern Cape. A common species. The photograph shows a male and female in a courtship display.

LONGHORN COWFISH – *Lactoria cornuta*

Attains 45 cm. Has two forward pointing spines on the head and two similar spines projecting from the bottom rear of the box-like carapace and a large fan-like tail. Usually olive to yellow or brown with pale blue spots in the centre of each segment of the protective case. Inhabits protected lagoons and coastal reefs. Usually encountered singly in weedy areas near reefs. Ranges in depth from 1-50 m. Diet consists of sand-dwelling invertebrates, exposed by blowing away the sand with water jetted from its mouth. Ranges throughout Indo-West Pacific, Red Sea, south to the Eastern Cape. An uncommon species.

THORNSPINE COWFISH (BACKSPINE COWFISH) – *Lactoria fornasini*

Attains 15 cm. The front and rear projections are much shorter than the previous species. Also has a thorn-like spine in the middle of the back. Colour varies considerably from yellow with bluish or mauve spots and scribbles on the head and body, to a dark brown patchy colour overlaid with mauve spots ringed in yellow. Changes colour to suit surroundings. Occurs singly or in pairs and frequents tropical lagoons and offshore reefs in depths of 1-40 m. Preys on bottom-dwelling invertebrates. Ranges throughout Indo-West Pacific, Red Sea, south to the Eastern Cape. An uncommon species.

Blaasops (puffers) – Family Tetraodontidae

Blaasops are divided into two groups; the Tetraodontinae and the Canthigasterinae; the latter group are known as sharpnose puffers, or tobies, and consists of small, often colourful fishes. Both groups have the ability, when threatened, to inflate themselves by swallowing water. As an additional protection, the skin and some internal organs contain a deadly poison called Tetrodotoxin. Blaasops are scaleless, lack pelvic fins and have fused teeth that form a beak that is used to crush prey. They swim in an almost clumsy manner.

EVILEYE BLAASOP – *Amblyrhynchotes honckenii*

Attains 30 cm. Has an elongated body, which tapers towards the tail. Upper surface is pale to dark brown, marked with various sized whitish to pale greenish-white spots. Underside is white. A horizontal yellow band may be present on the sides. Eyes are noticeably green with an orange iris. Often has three narrow dark bars on its back. Inhabits estuaries, rocky shores and offshore reefs ranging in depth from 0,3 m to 400 m. Preys on small fishes and invertebrates. Widespread throughout tropical Indo-West Pacific, extending to southern Cape. The most common blaasop along the east coast of southern Africa.

BLACKEDGED BLAASOP (IMMACULATE PUFFERFISH) *Arothron immaculatus*

Attains 30 cm. Grey to brown in colour. Prominent black blotch at pectoral fin base. Has a yellowish tail with dark blue or black border. Occurs on inshore and offshore reefs, in mangroves and in estuaries where it is encountered singly in depths of 1-30 m. Mostly active at night, feeding on bottom-living invertebrates. Widespread throughout Indo-West Pacific, Red Sea, south to the Eastern Cape. Relatively common.

BLACKSPOTTED BLAASOP – *Arothron nigropunctatus*

Attains 30 cm. A plump blaasop exhibiting a range of colours from grey to brown to bright yellow. Always has widely scattered black spots of varying size on the body. Inhabits coral and rocky reefs at depths of 10-25 m. Solitary and feeds on algae, sponges and sea squirts. Distributed throughout Indo-West Pacific, south to the Eastern Cape. A reasonably common yet shy species. As with other larger members of the family, it can inflict a nasty bite.

Boxy (male and female)

Longhorn cowfish

Thornspine cowfish

Evileye blaasop

Blackedged blaasop

Blackspotted blaasop

MAP BLAASOP (MAP OR MAPPA PUFFERFISH) – *Arothron mappa*
Attains 60 cm. A heavy-bodied blaasop with a rounded belly. General colour is whitish with greyish blotches covering the body. Irregular black lines and spots occur on the upper body. A large black blotch marks the pectoral fin base and irregular black lines radiate from the eye. A solitary species that inhabits offshore coral reefs. Usually found near caves and beneath overhangs. Feeds on algae, sponges and bottom-dwelling invertebrates. Widespread throughout Indo-West Pacific, occasionally extends to southern KwaZulu-Natal. Rather uncommon and shy.

EXQUISITE TOBY (BENNET'S TOBY) – *Canthigaster bennetti*
Attains 10 cm. Usually the upper side of body is brownish yellow to grey with numerous small orange spots and a scattering of small pale blue spots and lines. The lower body is white with red, orange and pale blue spots. The region around the eyes is orange-yellow with radiating blue lines. Prominent blue-edged, black elongated spot occurs at the base of dorsal fin. Inhabits shallow protected bays, lagoons and harbours, as well as offshore reefs. Adults often occur in pairs and are usually found on sand and rubble bottoms or in weedy areas. Ranges in depth between 1-30 m. Feeds on algae, sponges and invertebrates. Widespread throughout Indo-West Pacific, south to the Eastern Cape. An uncommon species.

HONEYCOMB TOBY – *Canthigaster janthinoptera*
Attains 9 cm. This small, rather secretive toby has an overall dark brown to orange-brown colour with close-set small bluish-white spots on the head and body. Males have short greenish lines radiating from the eye. Frequents the intertidal zone, inshore and offshore reefs to a depth of at least 30 m, where they may be seen hovering in caves or beneath overhangs. Feeds on a variety of algae, sponges and invertebrates. Widespread throughout Indo-West Pacific, south to the Eastern Cape. A common toby.

DOUBLELINED TOBY (RIVULTATED TOBY) – *Canthigaster rivulata*
Attains 18 cm. Double longitudinal stripe marks each side of the body, and join in front of the gill opening. The stripes are generally brown but are yellow around the pectoral fin base. The upper stripe often merges with dark brown spots and stripes on the upper body. The lower body is whitish with small close-set, elongated blue spots, and the tail is yellowish with blue stripes. Also has a distinctive yellow iris with a blue ring around it. Inhabits inshore and offshore reefs to a depth of 100 m, where it may occur singly or in pairs. Feeds on algae, sponges and bottom-dwelling invertebrates. Occurs throughout Indo-West Pacific, and south to the Eastern Cape. More common below 20 m in southern African waters.

Porcupinefishes – Family Diodontidae

Porcupinefishes have similar features to blaasops but are distinguished by the spines on the scales, and larger eyes. The spines are normally held flat, but when threatened the fish can inflate itself into a spiky ball by drawing water into its abdomen, in order to deter predators. Their front teeth are fused together to form a powerful beak, enabling it to crush various hard-shelled invertebrates. Most species are active at night and shelter in caves and in weedy areas during the day. They are capable of inflicting a severe bite if handled.

BALLOON PORCUPINEFISH (LONGSPINED PORCUPINEFISH) – *Diodon holocanthus*
Attains 29 cm. This particular species has a light brown to light olive overall colour and a white underside. Usually has brown blotches or bands on its back, with small black spots scattered between the blotches. The fins are pale yellow. It has a short brown vertical bar extending above and below each eye. The spines on this porcupinefish may be raised without inflation. Inhabits offshore reefs at depths of 3-100 m, where it occurs alone, hiding on reefs with dense growth or in seagrass beds. Feeds on sea urchins, molluscs and hermit crabs. Known from most sub-tropical and warm temperate seas. In South Africa, it ranges south to the Western Cape. An uncommon species, that retreats into a shelter if approached too closely.

PORCUPINEFISH (BLACKSPOTTED OR COMMON PORCUPINEFISH) – *Diodon hystrix*
Attains 65 cm. The largest member of the porcupinefish family. This fish has an elongated body which tapers towards the tail. The overall colour is light greyish-brown to olive, shading to a pale underside. Numerous close-set small black spots are scattered over the head and body. The fins are yellowish and also covered with small black spots. Usually hides during the day, but is occasionally seen swimming over the reef. Ranges in depths from 5-50 m. Feeds mainly on molluscs, sea urchins, crabs and hermit crabs. Known from most subtropical and warm temperate seas. In South Africa, it ranges south to the Western Cape. A rather shy and uncommon porcupinefish.

Map blaasop

Exquisite toby

Honeycomb toby

Doublelined toby

Balloon porcupinefish

Porcupinefish

NUDIBRANCHS

Nudibranchs, or seaslugs, are found in all of the world's oceans and are abundant in southern African waters. The variety of nudibranchs that live in this region can be attributed to the diversity of the marine environment. Although many species are found throughout the Indo-Pacific and to a lesser extent the Atlantic Ocean, certain species are endemic to southern Africa. This is good news for the nudibranch enthusiast as there is ample opportunity to admire the diversity of colour and pattern in these fascinating animals. Another encouraging aspect for an amateur nudibranch enthusiast is the fact that our knowledge of nudibranchs is limited. There are relatively few professional biologists worldwide specializing in the study of these animals. Consequently, observations made by scuba divers and snorkellers can play a valuable role in broadening our understanding.

HABITAT: Nudibranchs are found in a variety of habitats, from the intertidal zone to great depths, from the tropics where the greatest diversity occurs, to icy Antarctica. Many are easy to find, as they are brightly coloured. The more difficult ones to see are those that are well camouflaged, or small in size. Some good advice is to move slowly and allow the eye time to adjust to the environment. In so doing, there is a much better chance of detecting the movement or body outline of a nudibranch. For purposes of identification take note of certain key features, for example the pattern, whether the mantle is smooth or has nodules, the gill structure and the length of the animal. Look carefully under ledges and in the growth that covers the reef. The intertidal zone is another area awaiting exploration. The best time is at low spring tide. Remember that the more you look, the more you will discover as you develop a keener eye.

Nudibranch spawn ribbon

Mating *Nembrotha purpureolineata*

NUDIBRANCH TAXONOMY:

Phylum:	Mollusca
Class:	Gastropoda
Subclass:	Opisthobranchia
Orders:	Cephalaspidea (headshield slugs), Anaspidea (sea hares), Sacoglossa (sap-sucking slugs), Notaspidea (sidegill slugs), Nudibranchia (nudibranchs)
Suborders:	Doridina, Dendronotina,
(Nudibranchia)	Arminina, Aeolidina

The nudibranchs are the largest order in the subclass Opisthobranchia. The more frequently encountered species that occur along the south and east coasts of southern Africa have been included in this section. (Three members of the order Cephalaspidea, i.e. bubble shells, have been discussed because they are particularly common in the intertidal rock pools. These animals have a protective shell and a flattened headshield that they use for burrowing into the sand.)

DIET: Nudibranchs are carnivorous. Most have a rasp-like tongue called a radula and a strong pair of jaws made of chitin (hardened protein as in the carapace of crabs and crayfish). The tiny teeth that occur on the radula are arranged in unique patterns. The structure of these teeth is one of the factors taken into consideration in their identification and classification. Many nudibranchs feed on other invertebrates such as sponges, soft corals, anemones and hydroids. Certain species are specific about their diet and feed on only a single organism or a specific part of it, while others are generalized browsers. Our knowledge of the feeding habits of many species remains scant.

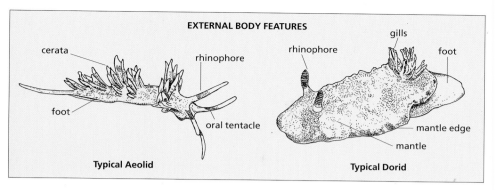

EXTERNAL BODY FEATURES

cerata

rhinophore

foot

oral tentacle

Typical Aeolid

gills

rhinophore

foot

mantle edge

mantle

Typical Dorid

RESPIRATION AND SENSORY ORGANS: The word nudibranch means 'naked gills'; an apt description as in most instances the external gills are situated dorsally, encircling the anus. Nudibranchs from the families Chromodorididae and Dorididae are able to retract their gills into a pouch or sheath when threatened or disturbed, whereas others, for example the Hexabranchidae, Polyceridae and Gymnodorididae, are unable to do so. In some families such as the Phyllidiidae, the gills are positioned in a groove between the mantle edge and the foot along the sides of the nudibranch. Animals from the order Dendronotina are characterized by pairs of simple or branched appendages situated along the side of the body, which effect gaseous exchange. In other families, for example the Zephyrinidae, Tergipedidae and Glaucidae, cerata (finger-like projections from the body) have evolved to perform various functions, one of which is respiration. Nudibranchs also have rhinophores, feeler-like protrusions near the front of the animal, which are used to relay chemosensory information.

LOCOMOTION: They move by crawling about slowly on a foot, which extends along the entire underside of the body, and comprises a flat, fleshy area. The foot produces sticky mucus to facilitate locomotion. The way in which movement is effected differs from species to species. Larger nudibranchs generally move by contracting their foot muscles from the posterior to the anterior end of the animal. Sand-dwellers do not rely on the muscular contractions – they utilize cilia, which are fine hair-like structures coordinated in a rowing-type action, to glide over the secreted mucus.

REPRODUCTION: All nudibranchs are hermaphroditic, ie. one animal can act as both male and female, making simultaneous fertilization possible. However, they are unable to self-fertilize and must find another mature animal in order to mate. Reproductive organs are situated on the right side of their necks. Nudibranchs line themselves up next to each other, facing in opposite directions, and exchange sperm packets. Nudibranchs are able to store the sperm until it is required to fertilize their eggs, which they lay in a mucous matrix on a substrate. These egg masses vary in size, shape and colour. The majority of nudibranchs lay their spawn ribbons in a spiral shape. Most eggs hatch into free-swimming larvae known as veligers, drifting with the currents until they come into contact with a particular food source, which prompts them to settle and metamorphose into juveniles. The planktonic stage allows for considerable mobility, as veligers can be transported great distances by ocean currents. Some eggs hatch into veliger larvae that develop fully inside the spawn ribbon, emerging as miniature adults. It is thought that nudibranchs have a very short life span – estimated to be from a month to a year or two.

DEFENCE: At the larval stage, most nudibranchs have a shell, but in the process of evolution the adults have lost this protection. As a result, some have developed various protective mechanisms. For example, nudibranchs from the Phyllidiidae are able to secrete toxic chemicals that make them unpalatable. Fish appear to link the bad taste of a nudibranch to its distinctive colour pattern and avoid it. Others, especially the aeolids, have the ability to feed on marine invertebrates that have stinging cells called nematocysts. The nudibranchs are not affected by this food source and are able to store the nematocysts in their cerata, to be used for defence. Many arminids and aeolids are not capable of stinging, but try to distract an attacker by shedding cerata, which they are able to regrow.

Camouflage is another way of preventing detection. For example an aeolid often looks like the hydroid on which it feeds, while a dorid may be the same colour as the sponge it feeds on. Others survive by burrowing under sand or hiding under ledges. Certain nudibranchs make use of the cover of darkness by generally feeding at night as this makes it difficult for predators to detect them. Some are able to flee by swimming away.

ORDER CEPHALASPIDEA

Family Hydatinidae (Bubble shells)

Known as bubble shells due to their rounded appearance. Not able to completely retract their bodies into the thin shell, which is strikingly coloured with a flattened spire. The large, delicate foot is visible at all times.

Hydatina amplustre (LINNAEUS, 1758)

Attains 4,5 cm. The shell has alternating pink and white spiral bands separated by a black line. Intensity of pink colouring is variable. Body colour is translucent and white. Has well-developed black eyes. Favours inshore reefs where sandy areas are interspersed with rocks. A specialized predator feeding on polychaete worms. Occurs throughout tropical Indo-Pacific to the Eastern Cape. An uncommon species.

Hydatina physis (ROSE-PETAL BUBBLE SHELL) (LINNAEUS, 1758)

Attains 5 cm. Animal is large in comparison to the shell. Body colour is light pink to reddish brown, lined with a fluorescent blue border. Has a fragile white shell with numerous spiral dark brown lines. Favours sandy patches in inshore rock pools. Occurs on offshore rocky reefs up to 25 m. Feeds on polychaete worms. Widespread throughout warm waters. Common from the Eastern Cape northwards.

Micromelo undata (BRUGUIÈRE, 1792)

Attains 3,5 cm. The white shell is less rounded than in *Hydatina* species. Has three brown spiral lines connected with brown wavy lines. Animal is opaque with numerous irregular and blurry white spots. The blue-green border is edged in yellow. Feeds on polychaete worms. Widely distributed throughout Indo-Pacific and the Caribbean Sea to a depth of 25 m. Common from Mozambique to the Eastern Cape.

ORDER NUDIBRANCHIA

Suborder Doridina

There are more species in this suborder than in all the other three suborders (Dendronotina, Arminina, Aeolidina) combined. They are variable in shape and size. The sides are not generally visible as they are covered by a mantle. Dorids have a pair of rhinophores and the anus is found on the back, surrounded by gills.

Family Hexabranchidae

Distinguished by the six gills around the anus. More than 20 species have been described and named.

Hexabranchus sanguineus (SPANISH DANCER) (RÜPPELL AND LEUCKART, 1828)

Attains 40 cm. Mottled with red, orange, or brown and white colouring. Common name stems from the impressive coloration and ability to swim with graceful undulating movements. The gills and rhinophores are orange. *Periclimenes imperator*, a tiny commensal shrimp, is often found living on it. Occurs from the intertidal zone to offshore reefs to a depth of 40 m. Feeds on sponges, marine worms, sea squirts and certain shells. Widespread throughout Indo-Pacific and the Red Sea. A common species.

Family Polyceridae

A large, diverse family that occurs mostly in tropical areas. Animals from this family tend to have long, thin bodies covered with low protuberances.

Nembrotha purpureolineata O'DONOGHUE, 1924

Attains 6 cm. Body is white with red and yellow areas dorsally. Numerous continuous or interrupted brown lines mark the body. Gills and rhinophores are deep red and have a purple base. Ranges in depth from 15-30 m. Feeds on sea squirts. Widespread throughout Indo-Pacific and the Red Sea. A common species.

Family Gymnodorididae

Voracious predators noted for the ability to move quickly. The gonad is separate from the digestive gland.

Gymnodoris rubropapulosa (BERGH, 1905)

Attains 6 cm. Translucent white body with numerous orange spots or rings that appear to be slightly raised. Body is elongate and raised in profile. The foot and anterior end has an orange border. Gills are small and predominantly orange. Rhinophores have a translucent white stalk with orange tips. Found on offshore reefs in depths of 10-20 m. Feeds on soft-bodied molluscs. Widespread throughout Indo-West Pacific, extending south to northern KwaZulu-Natal. An uncommon species.

Hydatina amplustre

Hydatina physis

Micromelo undata

Hexabranchus sanguineus

Nembrotha purpureolineata

Gymnodoris rubropapulosa

Family Dorididae

The family Dorididae is the largest of the nudibranch families and comprises numerous genera. Current classification of the dorids is under revision. All genera have retractable gills and rhinophores.

Doris sp.

Attains 4 cm. This undescribed species is distinguished by its yellow body, which is covered with numerous black tipped tubercles. In certain specimens, some of the tubercles are plain yellow. The gills and rhinophores are yellow at the base, changing to black at the tips. Found mainly on offshore reefs in depths from 15-35 m. Feeds on sponges. Known from Tanzania and southern Africa. Encountered on reefs off the coast of KwaZulu-Natal and in the cooler waters of the Eastern Cape. A reasonably common species.

Halgerda carlsoni RUDMAN, 1978

Attains 7 cm. Conspicuous as its colour and size make it easy to spot on the reef. The animal has a white mantle with numerous rounded, orange-tipped tubercles. In addition, the body is covered by an irregular scattering of small orange dots. The colouring of the gills and rhinophores is variable, as they may be white with fine black speckles, or so densely marked that they appear to be almost entirely black. Found in depths from 15-25 m. Feeds on sponges. Initially thought to be confined to the tropical western Pacific, however reports from Tanzania and South Africa, off the northern coast of KwaZulu-Natal, seem to indicate that the species is distributed throughout the Indo-West Pacific. An uncommon species.

Halgerda dichromis FAHEY AND GOSLINER, 1999

Attains 6 cm. This species is translucent white with irregular black markings in the hollows between the yellow ridges. In some specimens these ridges are pronounced, whereas in others the general body profile is flatter. The gills are white with brown colouring up the inner axes. The rhinophores have a white stalk dotted with a few brown markings and matching brown clubs. Colour variation occurs as certain animals have no black markings and are smaller. Both varieties are sometimes found in the same area. Found on offshore reefs in depths exceeding 20 m. Feeds on sponges. Occurs in the western Indian Ocean and along the south coast of KwaZulu-Natal and the Eastern Cape. A common nudibranch.

Halgerda tessellata (BERGH, 1880)

Attains 4 cm. A particularly beautiful nudibranch. Its mantle is covered with a pattern of yellow ridges and chocolate brown depressions with numerous fine white spots. The rhinophores are brown, while the gills are white with some brown markings. Found from the intertidal zone to a depth of 30 m. Feeds on sponges. Distributed throughout Indo-West Pacific, and occurs on the northern coast of KwaZulu-Natal. Originally described from Palau in the western Pacific Ocean. An uncommon species.

Halgerda toliara FAHEY AND GOSLINER, 1999

Attains 3 cm. The body is white overall with a yellow reticulated pattern. The intensity of the yellow patterning is variable and the lines generally become less distinct towards the mantle edge where fine cream or pale yellow spots occur. The rhinophores and gills are tipped with black. Usually found on offshore reefs at depths of between 15-30 m. Diet consists of sponges. Reported from the western Indian Ocean where it occurs in Madagascar and along the coast of KwaZulu-Natal. An uncommon species.

Halgerda wasinensis ELIOT, 1904

Attains 5 cm. A nudibranch that is not easily overlooked as it has striking colours. Its mantle is brown to black and dominated by bright yellow ridges. The mantle edge and foot are white with a number of black spots of variable size. Rhinophores are ringed with yellow at the base, and the stalks are translucent white with black markings. The clubs are predominantly black. Its gills are white with black colouring along the inner axes. Found on inshore and offshore reefs to a depth of 30 m. Diet consists of sponges. Occurs along the east coast of Africa and Madagascar and on the north coast of KwaZulu-Natal (specimens from this area tend to have broader yellow ridges that are more rounded). A common species.

Doris sp.

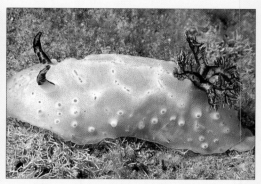

Halgerda carlsoni

Halgerda dichromis

Halgerda tessellata

Halgerda toliara

Halgerda wasinensis

Family Chromodorididae

The family Chromodorididae is particularly large and contains over three hundred nudibranchs. They are found in tropical and temperate seas throughout the Indo-West Pacific. They range considerably in size, with the largest species reaching in excess of 10 cm. The characteristic feature of this family is the soft flexible body that may have many vivid and eye-catching colours. The shape and arrangement of the radular teeth, used to scrape tissue from sponges when feeding, are a useful taxonomic tool in classifying nudibranchs.

Cadlinella ornatissima (RISBEC, 1928)

Attains 3,5 cm. Unusual appearance with pink-tipped white tubercles, which it is unable to throw off when disturbed. Mantle colour ranges from orange to pale yellow. Gills and tall rhinophores are white. Occurs on inshore and offshore reefs to a depth of 30 m. Feeds on sponges. Distributed throughout tropical Indo-Pacific and reported from the north coast of KwaZulu-Natal. An uncommon nudibranch.

Ceratosoma tenue ABRAHAM, 1876

Attains 12 cm. Characterized by three lobes fringed by either a continuous or broken purple line. In addition, a similarly coloured 'tongue' protrudes from behind the gills and may function as a defence lure, attracting potential predators to the part of the body where unappetising chemicals such as toxins, extracted from their food, are stored. The colour of this nudibranch varies from orange to brown and has patches of white mottling. Some specimens have mauve spots. The rhinophores are yellow or orange with white flecks and purple tipping. The tall gills are highly branched and streaked with red. It is found on offshore reefs at a depth of 25 m and feeds on sponges. Occurs throughout tropical Indo-West Pacific, and off the coast of KwaZulu-Natal and the eastern Cape. Not commonly seen.

Chromodoris africana ELIOT, 1904

Attains 7,5 cm. Displays an impressive combination of colours, making it one of the easier nudibranchs to spot. It is white with a broad, orange mantle edge. Three black lines run longitudinally, with the outer lines joining in front of the rhinophores at the anterior end, and posteriorly behind the gills. The central black line marks the mid-line of the nudibranch and runs from in front of the rhinophores to the gill area. The rhinophores and gills are orange. Occurs on inshore and offshore reefs to a depth of 30 m and feeds on sponges. Found in the Red Sea and western Indian Ocean and seen along the south coast of KwaZulu-Natal, sometimes in large numbers. A common species.

Chromodoris annulata ELIOT, 1904

Attains 10 cm. Translucent white and covered with yellow or orange spots. The mantle is edged in purple. Two purple lines further decorate the central section. The one encircles the rhinophores, whereas the other highlights the gill area. In some specimens these lines do not form a complete circle. Found from intertidal rock pools to offshore reefs to a depth of 30 m. Diet consists of sponges. Occurs along the coast of East Africa and has also been reported from Thailand, as well as the Red and Arabian seas. Known in southern Africa from Mozambique to the Eastern Cape. A common species.

Chromodoris boucheti RUDMAN, 1982

Attains 6 cm. The body colour is bluish white overall with a medial black line from between the rhinophores to the gills. A thicker black line encircles the body leaving a distinct white mantle edge. Further thin black lines occur on the central part of the mantle, but the exact positioning and number of these lines is variable. Each rhinophore club is yellow with a white stalk. The gills are white at their base with yellow tips. Black lines fringe both the inside and outside edges of each gill, although the line does not usually extend to the tip. Inhabits offshore reefs to a depth of 35 m. Feeds on sponges. Distributed throughout the western Indian Ocean and also found off the south coast of KwaZulu-Natal, where numerous specimens are often seen feeding together. A reasonably common species.

Chromodoris conchyliata YONOW, 1984

Attains 3,5 cm. White overall, the central part of the mantle is purple and scattered with numerous yellowish pustules. A cream band encircles the mantle. The rhinophores and gills are white and red. Moves by flapping its mantle up and down as it crawls along, revealing the deep purple colour on the underside. Occurs from the intertidal zone to offshore reefs down to a depth of 25 m and feeds on sponges. Reported from Kenya, Sri Lanka, Thailand and South Africa, where the distribution extends south to the Eastern Cape. This uncommon species may be confused with *Chromodoris geometrica* (see overleaf).

Cadlinella ornatissima

Ceratosoma tenue

Chromodoris africana

Chromodoris annulata

Chromodoris boucheti

Chromodoris conchyliata

Chromodoris geometrica
RISBEC, 1928

Attains 3,5 cm. This is a relatively small nudibranch variable in colour, as the background colour of the mantle ranges from pale brown to purple. The mantle is decorated with numerous cream pustules of various sizes and is bordered by a white band. The gills and tall rhinophores are white and green, or greenish yellow. This species is part of a group with a large anterior mantle skirt, which is raised upwards and downwards as the animal crawls along. Ranges from the intertidal zone to offshore reefs to a depth of 25 m. Feeds on sponges. Widely distributed throughout Indo-West Pacific, and known in southern Africa from Mozambique to the Eastern Cape. This reasonably common nudibranch is similar to *Chromodoris conchyliata*, but the latter has gills and rhinophores, which are white and red in colour.

Chromodoris fidelis
(KELAART, 1858)

Attains 3 cm. The mantle of this small nudibranch is smooth and white with an orange margin. The two colours are separated by a red scalloped pattern, with spaces between the scallops. The profile is flattened and the colour variable. In some specimens the patterning is confined to the edge of the mantle, whereas in others the patterning joins at the midline. The tall rhinophores and gills are black. This nudibranch occurs from the intertidal zone to offshore reefs to a depth of 35 m and feeds on sponges. Distributed throughout Indo-West Pacific and known in southern Africa from Mozambique to KwaZulu-Natal. An uncommon nudibranch.

Chromodoris geminus
RUDMAN, 1987

Attains 6 cm. A particularly attractive nudibranch. The body has three distinct rows of deep purple spots, each of which is surrounded by an opaque white ring. It is characterized by a wide marginal ring of four distinctive colours – a band of yellow on the inside, followed by white, then greyish purple, and finally another white band at the mantle edge. The rhinophores are tipped with yellow and the gills are white with a grey edge. Occurs in depths not exceeding 25 m. Feeds on sponges. Found throughout the tropical Indian Ocean and reported from Mozambique to the Eastern Cape. This relatively flat chromodorid is uncommon and moves in an unusual way as it flaps its mantle edge up and down as it crawls along. May be confused with *Chromodoris* cf. *geminus* (see below).

Chromodoris cf. geminus
RUDMAN, 1987

Attains 6 cm. The mantle is a deep shade of yellow and its spots are quite variable in size. The mantle edge has a double white and purple border. The rhinophores and gills are purple and white. *Chromodoris* cf. *geminus* 'ripples' its sides in an irregular way when moving. It may well be a new species. Found on offshore reefs to a depth of 30 m and most likely feeds on sponges. Occurs along the south coast of KwaZulu-Natal and the Eastern Cape. A reasonably common and colourful species that resembles *Chromodoris geminus*.

Chromodoris hamiltoni
RUDMAN, 1977

Attains 6 cm. Readily identified by its bright blue mantle colour, although some specimens are much paler. Generally the mantle has three dominant longitudinal black lines; however some specimens lack the central black line and have a varying number of finer parallel, broken black lines instead. A further variation occurs in that the central area may have patches of orange or light brown. The mantle has a broad orange marginal band that may be lined with white on the inner edge. The rhinophores and gills are also orange. Inhabits both inshore and offshore reefs to depths of between 10-25 m. Feeds on sponges. Found off the coast of East Africa, Mozambique and KwaZulu-Natal. A very common species.

Chromodoris heatherae
GOSLINER, 1994

Attains 1,5 cm. This small nudibranch is translucent white in colour, usually with large red spots. The mantle is fringed by an opaque white band and in some cases there is an irregular yellow line on the inside of the mantle edge. The rhinophores and gills are white. Found on rocky reefs in temperate waters, occurring from the intertidal zone to a depth of 30 m. Feeds on sponges. Found in the Eastern Cape, extending south to the Atlantic coast of the Cape Peninsula. Appears to be an endemic species that is reasonably common.

Chromodoris geometrica

Chromodoris fidelis

Chromodoris geminus

Chromodoris cf. *geminus*

Chromodoris hamiltoni

Chromodoris heatherae

Chromodoris tinctoria
(RÜPPELL AND LEUCKART, 1828)
Attains 8 cm. A particularly variable nudibranch in terms of its colour. Interestingly, after investigation, it has been found that many differently named nudibranchs (for example, *Chromodoris alderi, Chromodoris inopinata, Doris reticulata*) have identical internal anatomy indicating that they are all one species. The body is opaque white with pink to red reticulate markings. The mantle border is also variable and two forms occur off the coast of southern Africa. More commonly, the red and white reticulate pattern covering the mantle area is edged with a yellow border. In certain other specimens this yellow marginal band has a distinct white inner border with small patches of reticulated patterning. The rhinophores and gills are purple and white. Inhabits offshore reefs to a depth of 30 m. Diet consists of sponges. Ranges throughout tropical Indo-West Pacific and is reasonably common.

Glossodoris atromarginata
(CUVIER, 1804)
Attains 7 cm. The mantle is variable in colour as it ranges from cream to a light yellow-brown with white speckles. It has a black marginal border bounded on each side with a fine pale white band. The body is elongate and flattened in profile. The body margin undulates as it moves. The rhinophores and gills are cream and black. The gills vibrate as the animal crawls along, which is characteristic of the *Glossodoris* genus of nudibranchs. Found on both inshore and offshore reefs to a depth of 30 m. Feeds on sponges. Widely distributed throughout the Pacific and Indian Oceans and found off the coast of northern KwaZulu-Natal. A common nudibranch.

Glossodoris cinta
(BERGH, 1888)
Attains 6 cm. This nudibranch is variable in colour. The form that commonly occurs in northern KwaZulu-Natal is rosy brown with fine white spots. The mantle has a striking marginal band of yellow and black. This is a marked difference from species that occur elsewhere in the world as they have a bluish-white edging. The rhinophores are pale purple with fine white speckles, while the gills are pale purple with white spots and charcoal edges. This nudibranch is able to discharge a white fluid when irritated. Occurs on shallow reefs to a depth of 25 m and feeds on sponges. Distributed throughout Indo-West Pacific. A reasonably common species.

Glossodoris pallida
(RÜPPELL AND LEUCKART, 1830)
Attains 3,5 cm. This small nudibranch has a translucent white mantle and a thin lemon yellow marginal band. The mantle has a few opaque markings and the rhinophores and gills are white with lemon yellow tips. Although it occurs on offshore reefs, it seems to prefer the subtidal zone in the 10-15 m depth range. Feeds on sponges. Found throughout tropical Indo-West Pacific and occurs in the warmer waters off northern KwaZulu-Natal. A common species.

Glossodoris sp.
Attains 3,5 cm. Uniformly white with a cream marginal border. The rhinophores and gills are also white. Found more commonly in the 15-25 m depth range, although it has also been seen on deeper reefs in 40 m and feeds on sponges. This undescribed species occurs along the south coast of KwaZulu-Natal and the Eastern Cape and appears to be endemic. Common and similar to *Glossodoris pallida*, but has no irregular markings.

Glossodoris symmetricus
RUDMAN, 1990
Attains 4,5 cm. Unusual colouring as it is white with symmetrical opaque white markings, which is similar to those found on *Glossodoris pallida*. The mantle edge, rhinophores and gills are bright red and this provides a striking contrast to the body colour. The animal tends to 'frill' the mantle edge as it crawls along. Found on both inshore and offshore reefs to a depth of 30 m. Feeds on sponges. Occurs throughout the Indo-West Pacific and is reasonably common from Mozambique to the Eastern Cape.

Chromodoris tinctoria

Glossodoris atromarginata

Glossodoris cinta

Glossodoris pallida

Glossodoris sp.

Glossodoris symmetricus

Glossodoris undaurum
Attains 7 cm. The white mantle is marked with numerous opaque white blotches of various shapes and sizes. This makes it a difficult subject to capture on film as the photograph often looks out of focus, when in fact a true image of the animal has been reproduced. Towards the edge of the mantle, the blotches are generally absent and the marginal rim or band ranges from bright yellow to cream. The rhinophores are white with pale yellow tips, while the white gills are tipped with orange. Although it does occur on inshore reefs, it is most commonly found on offshore reefs to a depth of 20 m. Feeds on sponges. Occurs off western Australia and along the east coast of Africa extending to the Eastern Cape in the south. A reasonably common species.

Hypselodoris bullockii
(COLLINGWOOD, 1881)
Attains 6 cm. This species has a high body profile and appears to have a wide colour range as it varies from white through to bright pink. The animal is so smooth that it looks as though it has been polished. Typically the mantle has a distinct thin white edge; however some specimens are lined with a purple border. The rhinophores and gills are generally orange or yellow with a purplish base. Inhabits both inshore and offshore reefs in the 10-20 m depth range. Feeds on sponges. It is of interest that this nudibranch was originally described from the South China Sea. Distributed throughout the tropical regions of the western Pacific and eastern Indian Oceans and also known from northern KwaZulu-Natal. An uncommon species.

Hypselodoris carnea
(BERGH, 1889)
Attains 3,5 cm. Not a particularly attractive species. It is easily overlooked as it is pale in colour. Has numerous thin translucent white lines that run longitudinally. The mantle is marked with numerous brownish-red spots and is edged with a purple border. The rhinophores and sides of the gills are orange. Found from the intertidal zone to offshore reefs to a depth of 40 m. Diet consists of sponges. Occurs along the coast of KwaZulu-Natal and the Eastern Cape and has also been recorded from Mauritius. A common nudibranch, very similar in colour to *Hypselodoris capensis*.

Hypselodoris fucata
GOSLINER AND JOHNSON, 1999
Attains 5 cm. This nudibranch is recognized by its beige mantle with alternating red and white longitudinal lines, which are not always continuous. The sides of the animal are marked with thicker broken red lines, and the mantle is circled with a distinct broken purple band followed by a thin yellow marginal rim. The rhinophores are orange and the gills are white with an orange edging. It occurs on both inshore and offshore reefs to a depth of 30 m. Feeds on sponges. Apparently endemic to the east coast of South Africa and particularly common on the south coast of KwaZulu-Natal.

Hypselodoris maculosa
(PEASE, 1871)
Attains 3,5 cm. Easy to overlook because of its small size, flattened profile and colours that tend to blend in with the reef. The mantle is pale pink or orange with thin longitudinal broken white lines and an orange marginal border. Small irregular purple dots decorate the body, while the anterior end and foot have finer, more concentrated, white dots. The rhinophores are white with orange bands and these colours are repeated in the small gills. Ranges from the intertidal zone down to a depth of 20 m. Feeds on sponges. Occurs in the tropical Indo-West Pacific and found along the Mozambique coast, KwaZulu-Natal, extending south into Cape waters. A reasonably common nudibranch.

Hypselodoris rudmani
GOSLINER AND JOHNSON, 1999
Attains 2,5 cm. This nudibranch is translucent white with scattered opaque cream markings and irregular dark brown spots, which are more concentrated towards the cream mantle edge. The mantle and foot have a deep blue marginal band, which is not continuous. The white gills are edged in orange or red, and this colour is repeated in the rhinophore clubs. Inhabits the intertidal zone to a depth of 25 m. Feeds on sponges. Occurs off the coast of KwaZulu-Natal and the Eastern Cape. An uncommon species.

Glossodoris undaurum

Hypselodoris bullockii

Hypselodoris carnea

Hypselodoris fucata

Hypselodoris maculosa

Hypselodoris rudmani

Hypselodoris sp.

Attains 6 cm. This undescribed species has an orange mantle with a dark brown medial line. The line, bordered by white, is normally continuous, but may be broken. A similarly coloured line stretches from rhinophore to rhinophore around the body and forms a 'horse-shoe' shape with its base between the orange rhinophores. The sides of the body are orange and may be decorated with a few black spots encircled with white. The tall gills are white with thin orange streaks up the outer axes. The foot is particularly striking as it matches the mantle in colour and has a variable pattern of stripes and spots. It inhabits inshore and offshore reefs to a depth of 25 m. Most likely feeds on sponges. Appears to be an endemic species to the coast of KwaZulu-Natal and is reasonably common.

Risbecia pulchella   (RÜPPELL AND LEUCKART, 1828)

Attains 10 cm. Has a pink mantle with scattered white patches. Covered with yellow dots. The mantle has a thin purple marginal band. The rhinophores are pink and the gills are white with purple axes. Often found moving about in pairs with one animal moving directly behind the leader with its head placed on the 'tail' directly in front of it. The animal in tandem is usually smaller. This 'trailing' behaviour is characteristic of the *Risbecia* genus. Occurs from the intertidal zone to offshore reefs to a depth of 30 m. Feeds on sponges. Distributed throughout the Indian Ocean and occurs in the Red, Arabian and Andaman Seas as well as from East Africa to the south coast of KwaZulu-Natal. An uncommon species.

Thorunna horologia   RUDMAN, 1984

Attains 1,5 cm. May be overlooked as it is so small. Best viewed underwater with a magnifying glass. White with a yellow marginal ring with red on the outside. Marked indentation on the body where the marginal band is more pronounced – this is reflected in its name, which relates to the Latin word for an hourglass. Rhinophores and gills are orange and white. The foot has a purple edge. Found at depths of between 8-25 m and feeds on sponges. Reported from Tanzania and KwaZulu-Natal. Common.

Family Dendrodorididae

A small family comprising mostly tropical species. Species have no radula or jaws. Food is consumed by sucking up the prey using a long, oral tube. The characteristic body shape is oval.

Dendrodoris denisoni   (ANGAS, 1864)

Attains 6 cm. Blends in with the growth on the reef. Numerous tubercles occur on its back. Brown with groups of blue spots. In certain animals these spots may be very small, or even absent. Inhabits pools in the intertidal zone through to offshore reefs to a depth of 25 m. It feeds on sponges. Occurs throughout the Indo-West Pacific in both warm temperate and tropical waters and is reasonably common.

Family Phyllidiidae

This family comprises approximately 70 species. These species have rigid bodies and skins toughened with tiny rods called spicules. Gills are hidden from view in a series of folds along the underside of the body. The texture is interesting as they are often covered with brightly coloured tubercles. The dominant colours are yellow, orange, black and white. These nudibranchs are notorious for their ability to extract toxic chemicals from the sponges they eat, storing them for defence against predators.

Phyllidia ocellata   CUVIER, 1804

Attains 6 cm. Variable in colour and texture, as the tubercles are of different shapes and sizes. Most common colour form occurring on the coast of KwaZulu-Natal and the Eastern Cape is yellow, black and white. The orange, black and white form does occur, but it is not common. The rhinophores are yellow. Gills are situated in a groove between foot and mantle. Inhabits offshore reefs to a depth of 35 m. Feeds on sponges. Found throughout tropical Indo-West Pacific, including the Rea Sea. Reasonably common.

Phyllidia varicosa   LAMARCK, 1801

Attains 8,5 cm. Characterized by distinct longitudinal ridges of pale grey, which are not always continuous, and decorated with bright yellow tubercles. Rows are separated by black areas resulting in a striking pattern. Numerous radial ridges of similar colour and design extend towards margins of the mantle. Rhinophores are yellow. Gills are situated in a series of folds between the foot and mantle. Occurs in the intertidal zone and on offshore reefs to a depth of 30 m. Feeds on sponges. Widespread throughout tropical Indo-Pacific Ocean, including the Red Sea. Known in southern Africa from Mozambique to the Eastern Cape. A common species.

Hypselodoris sp.

Risbecia pulchella

Thorunna horologia

Dendrodoris denisoni

Phyllidia ocellata

Phyllidia varicosa

Phyllidiella zeylanica
(KELAART, 1859)

Attains 6 cm. Black in colour with numerous white ridges that support fine white tubercles. Most of the ridges are continuous, curving to meet at the end of the animal's body. The rhinophores are black. The gills are situated in a groove between the foot and the mantle. Occurs to a depth of 25 m. Feeds on sponges. Distributed throughout the Indian Ocean. A reasonably common species.

Suborder Dendronotina

Comprises a small number of animals, variable in shape and size. The rhinophores have cup-like sheaths and the mantle skirt is either small or non-existent. A series of gills occur along the edge of the body.

Family Bornellidae

The Bornellidae have long, slender bodies. Finger-like extensions protrude from each side, with much larger, taller, similar looking protrusions surrounding the rhinophores.

Bornella anguilla
JOHNSON, 1983

Attains 8 cm. Long, slender body with a brown, orange, yellow and white pattern. Numerous paired, paddle-like appendages occur along the body. Occurs on reefs shallower than 25 m. Feeds on hydroids. Occurs throughout Indo-West Pacific and from Mozambique to southern KwaZulu-Natal. Uncommon.

Suborder Arminina

Smallest suborder and relatively well represented in southern Africa. Gills are situated along sides of the body.

Family Zephyrinidae

These animals have well-developed cerata, which are used for digestion, respiration and defence. They feed exclusively on moss, or lace, animals (bryozoans).

Janolus capensis
BERGH, 1907

Attains 7 cm. Densely covered with well-developed beige cerata with light blue tips. Quick to throw off cerata when disturbed. Found from intertidal zone to a depth of 40 m. Feeds on bryozoans. An endemic species that occurs on both sides of the Cape Peninsula, extending to Eastern Cape. A common species.

Suborder Aeolidina

The second largest suborder. Characterized by a long, narrow body. Capable of moving relatively quickly. Have cerata, which are used as a digestive gland extension and assist in respiratory functions. Many collect nematocysts from cnidarians and store them in an undischarged state in the tips of the cerata for defence.

Family Tergipedidae

Comprises a small number of different species, which typically feed on hydroids and corals.

Cuthona sp.

Attains 2,5 cm. Brightly coloured pink body and rhinophores, and yellow tipped red cerata. Has yet to be described. Found to a depth of 25 m. Browses on hydroids and occurs along the coast of KwaZulu-Natal and the Eastern Cape. Probably also occurs in the Indo-West Pacific. A reasonably common species.

Family Glaucidae

Many glaucids are able to 'farm' zooxanthellae, which are photosynthesizing organisms able to convert the energy of the sun into sugars, thereby feeding both the host and themselves. They have the ability to throw off their cerata when disturbed.

Phyllodesmium sp.

Attains 4,5 cm. The white body has long curved transparent cerata, revealing the cream digestive gland. They are able to shed cerata when disturbed. Found from the intertidal zone to offshore reefs to a depth of 20 m. Feeds on soft corals. Occurs off the coast of KwaZulu-Natal. A reasonably common species.

Pteraeolidia ianthina
(ANGAS, 1864)

Attains 15 cm. Long, thin cream body with bluish spots. Clusters of cerata, which can be raised vertically if animal is disturbed, are arranged in twin series of fans along the body. Their colour ranges from brown, purple, to white. Rhinophore tips are purple. Ranges from intertidal zone to a depth of 30 m. Feeds on nutrients provided by zooxanthellae and hydroids. Occurs throughout Indo-West Pacific. Common.

Phyllidiella zeylanica

Bornella anguilla

Janolus capensis

Cuthona sp.

Phyllodesmium sp.

Pteraeolidia ianthina

Abdomen – belly

Aeolid – a nudibranch belonging to the suborder Aeolidina

Aggregation – group of fish, not all swimming in the same direction, ie. as opposed to a shoal

Algae – unicellular photosynthetic plants

Anal fin – a fin just below the tail

Anterior – the front or head

Barbel – a fleshy projection near the mouth, used for taste, smell or touch

Bony fishes – fishes with a true bony skeleton

Brackish – water that is neither totally fresh, nor as salty as pure seawater

Carapace – bony or chitinous shield covering part or all of the back of certain animals

Carnivorous – feeding on animals

Cartilaginous – composed of cartilage; descriptive of fishes that lack true bony skeletons, eg. sharks, skates and rays

Caudal fin – the unpaired fin at the tail

Caudal peduncle – the narrow region that attaches the caudal fin to the body

Cerata – finger-like extensions arising from the mantle of certain nudibranchs, which function in digestion, respiration and defence

Clubs – the rounded tips of some rhinophores

Cnidarian – animals belonging to the phylum Cnidaria – for example jellyfish, anemones and hydroids

Commensal – an organism that lives together with another species without harming it

Compressed – flattened shape of body from side to side

Crustaceans – a group of mostly aquatic invertebrates including crabs, shrimps and lobsters

Deep-bodied – shape of fish where the height is greater in relation to the length

Depressed – flattened from top to bottom

Demersal – living close to the seabed

Disc – fused head and fin region of some depressed fish

Disc-width – the 'wingspan' of rays

Dorid – a nudibranch belonging to the suborder Doridina

East Coast – the coastline including the Eastern Cape from East London northwards to Mozambique

Eelgrass – a flowering marine plant that occurs in bays and estuaries

Elongated – shape where the length is greater in relation to the height

Endemic – limited to a particular geographic region

Estuary – the widening channel of a river where it nears the sea, and where salinities fluctuate

Family – a major entity in the classification of animals and plants, consisting of related genera

Filamentous – thread-like, eg. algae

Fins – fleshy projections used for steering

Genus – a group of closely related animal or plant species with similar characteristics, usually containing several species

Gill – respiratory organ

Gill cover – bony plate protecting the gills of bony fish

Gill opening – opening behind the head protected by the gill cover through which inhaled water is passed

Gill raker – projection on gill arches that filters food particles from water

Habitat – environment of an organism

Herbivorous – feeding on plant material

Hermaphrodite – an individual that possesses functional male and female reproductive organs

Indo-Pacific – embracing the Indian and western Pacific Oceans

Initial phase – sub-adult phase

Intertidal zone – shoreline between high and low water

Invertebrate – animal without backbone

Lateral line – a canal or row of sensory pores in the skin along the body of fishes, responsible for detecting sound

Lappet – a little flap

Lunate – shaped like the crescent of a new moon

Mantle – a layer of tissue on the dorsal (back) surface of the gastropod primarily responsible for the secretion of the shell in molluscs

Median fins – the fins in the median plane, hence the dorsal, anal and caudal fins

Midwater – between surface and seabed

Mollusc – an invertebrate belonging to the Phylum Mollusca, which includes mussels, snails, chitons, squid etc.

Mucus – slimy fluid produced by mucous glands in the skin

Sulphur damsel

Nematocyst – stinging cells found in cnidarians – for example, hydroids, sea anemones

Omnivorous – feeding on plants and animals

Opisthobranch – one of the subclasses of the class Gastropoda, including nudibranchs, sea hares and bubble shells

Oral tentacles – sensory feelers on either side of the mouth

Patch reef – reef established upon irregularities of the seabed, existing independently of a major reef formation

Pectoral – chest or breast region

Peduncle – *see* caudal peduncle

Pelagic – living in the open sea

Pelvic – related to the pelvis or hind limb, posterior to the belly

Pharyngeal teeth – teeth located in the throat behind the gills

Pinnacle – high, slender rock formation

Plankton – tiny animals (zooplankton) or plants (phythoplankton) that float or drift in the water

Polychaete worms – a group of marine worms related to earth worms

Posterior – the rear

Pustules – irregular, wart-like projections or lumps

Pustules – irregular, slightly elevated markings

Radula – ribbon tongue bearing rows of teeth in a mollusc

Ray – a cartilaginous and jointed fin support

Rhinophores – paired chemical sensors on the top surface of the anterior (head) end of some molluscs

Scutes – external bony plate

Shoal – group of fish swimming in the same direction

South Coast – coastline including Western and Eastern Cape, from Cape Town to East London

Species – the fundamental unit in the classification of animals and plants consisting of a population of individuals that freely interbreed

Spine – a sharp, unjointed projection, often part of fin

Spiracles – respiratory opening

Substratum – a layer (ie. rock) or solid object to which an animal or plant can attach itself

Subtidal – below the lowest level on the shore reached by the tides

Symbiosis – relationship between two organisms, which is of mutual benefit

Taxonomy – the study of classification of plants and animals

Terminal phase – sexually mature adult

Tubercles – a low, conical, rounded or uneven projection; like a wart

Tunicates – a group of minute, primitive, sedentary marine animals that have a sac-like unsegmented body

Ventral – the lower region or underside

Water column – the body of water between the seabed and surface

Zooplankton – the animal component of plankton suspended in the water column

Zooxanthellae – unicellular algae that are symbiotic in the bodies of some animals

Allen, G & Steene, R 1987 *Reef Fishes of the Indian Ocean.* T.F.H. Publications Inc. USA

Allen, G & Steene, R & Allen, M 1998. *A Guide to Angelfishes and Butterflyfishes.* Odyssey Publishing USA

Branch, G & M 1981. *The Living Shores of Southern Africa.* C. Struik , Cape Town

Branch, G & M, Griffiths, C & Beckley, L 1994. *Two Oceans – A Guide to the Marine Life of Southern Africa.* David Philip Publishers, Cape Town

Burgess, W, Axelrod, H & Hunziler, R 1988. *Dr Burgess's Atlas of Marine Aquarium Fishes.* T.F.H. Publications Inc. USA

Cole, N 1989. *Nudibranchs of the South Pacific.* Neville Coleman's Sea Australia Resource Centre, Springwood, Queensland

Compagno, I, Ebert, D & Smale, M 1989. *Guide to the Sharks and Rays of Southern Africa.* Struik Publishers, Cape Town

Debelius, H 1996. *Nudibranchs and Sea Snails, Indo-Pacific Field Guide.* IKAN, Frankfurt, Germany

Debelius, H 1999. *Indian Ocean Reef Guide.* IKAN, Frankfurt, Germany

Debelius, H 1998. *Red Sea Reef Guide.* IKAN, Frankfurt Germany

Gosliner, T 1987. *Nudibranchs of Southern Africa. A Guide to Opisthoranch Molluscs of Southern Africa.* Sea Challengers, Monterey, California

Human, P 1989. *Reef Fish Identification.* New World Publications USA

Kuiter, R H 1998. *A Photo Guide to Fishes of the Maldives.* Atoll Editions Australia

Kuiter, R H 1992. *Tropical Reef Fishes of the Western Pacific – Indonesia and Adjacent Waters.* Penerbit P.T. Indonesia

Last, P R & Stevens, J D 1994. *Sharks and Rays of Australia.* CSIRO Australia

Lieske, E & Myers, R 1994. *Collins Pocket Guide: Coral Reef Fishes.* Harper Collins Publishers, Johannesburg

Marshall, J G & Willan, R C 1999. *Nudibranchs of Heron Island, Great Barrier Reef.* Backhuys Publishers, Leiden, Holland

Smith, M & Heemstra, P (eds) 1988. *Smith's Sea Fishes.* Southern Book Publishers, Johannesburg

Van der Elst, R 1986. *Struik Pocket Guide Series: Sharks and Stingrays.* Struik Publishers, Cape Town

Van der Elst, R 1988. *A Guide to the Common Sea Fishes of Southern Africa.* Struik Publishers, Cape Town

Van der Elst, R 2000. *Everyone's Guide to Sea Fishes of Southern Africa.* Struik Publishers, Cape Town

Van der Elst, R 1999. *Sasol First Field Guide to Fishes of Southern Africa.* Struik Publishers, Cape Town

Wells, F E & Bryce, C W 1993. *Sea Slugs of Western Australia.* Western Australian Museum, Perth

Halgerda wasinensis

INDEX TO SCIENTIFIC NAMES

Naso unicornis	98
Naso vlamingii	98
Neoniphon argenteus	26
Neopomacentrus cyanomos	70
Oplegnathus robinsoni	66
Ostracion cubicus	106
Oxycheilinus bimaculatus	76
Oxycheilinus digramma	76
Oxymonacanthus longirostris	104
Pachymetopon aeneum	50
Pachymetopon grande	50
Pagellus bellottii natalensis	50
Papilloculiceps longiceps	30
Paracaesio sordidus	44
Paracaesio xanthura	44
Paracanthurus hepatus	96
Paraluteres prionurus	104
Parapercis schauinslandi	90
Parapercis xanthozona	88
Parascorpis typus	56
Parupeneus cyclostomus	56
Parupeneus pleurostigma	58
Pervagor janthinosoma	104
Petrus rupestris	50
Plagiotremus rhinorhynchos	90
Platax teira	56
Platycephalus indicus	30
Plectorhinchus chubbi	38
Plectorhinchus gibbosus	40
Plectorhinchus plagiodesmus	40
Plectorhinchus vittatus	40
Plectroglyphidodon dickii	70
Plectroglyphidodon johnstonianus	70
Plectroglyphidodon lacrymatus	70
Plotosus lineatus	24
Polyamblyodon gibbosum	50
Polysteganus praeorbitalis	52
Polysteganus undulosus	52
Pomacanthus chrysurus	58
Pomacanthus maculosus	58
Pomacentrus pavo	72
Pomacentrus sulfureus	72
Pomacentrus trichourus	72
Pomadasys furcatum	40
Pomadasys kaakan	40
Pomadasys multimaculatum	42
Pomatomus saltatrix	38
Porcostoma dentata	52
Poroderma africanum	18
Pseudanthias fasciatus	32
Pseudobalistes fuscus	102
Pseudocaranx dentex	64
Pseudocheilinus evanidus	78
Pseudocheilinus hexataenia	80
Pseudochromis melas	36
Pseudochromis natalensis	36
Pseudodax moluccanus	82

Pseudojuloides cerasinus	84
Ptereleotris heteroptera	96
Ptereleotris zebra	96
Pterois radiata	28
Rhabdosargus globiceps	52
Rhina ancylostoma	18
Rhincodon typus	16
Rhinecanthus rectangulus	102
Rhinomuraena quaesita	20
Rhinopias eschmeyeri	30
Rhynchobatus djiddensis	18
Scartella emargineta	92
Scarus frenatus	86
Scarus scaber	86
Scarus tricolor	86
Scolopsis ghanam	54
Scolopsis vosmeri	54
Scomber japonicus	100
Scomberoides commersonnianus	64
Scorpaenopsis diabolus	28
Scorpaenopsis oxycephala	30
Seriola lalandi	66
Seriola rivoliana	66
Serranus cabrilla	36
Siganus luridus	100
Siganus stellatus	98
Solenostomus cyanopterus	28
Sphyraena jello	88
Sphyraena putnamiae	88
Sphyrna lewini	18
Spondyliosoma emarginatum	52
Stegostoma fasciatum	16
Stethojulis interrupta	84
Synodus jaculum	24
Terapon jarbua	36
Thalassoma genivittatum	84
Thalassoma hardwicke	86
Thalassoma purpureum	84
Thalassoma trilobatum	86
Trachinotus africanus	64
Trachinotus blochii	64
Trachinotus botla	64
Trachurus trachurus	66
Triaenodon obesus	16
Tylosurus crocodilus crocodilus	24
Umbrina canariensis	58
Valenciennea helsdingenii	94
Valenciennea sexguttata	94
Xanthichthys auromarginatus	102
Xanthichthys lineopunctatus	104
Zebrasoma gemmatum	98

NUDIBRANCHS

Bornella anguilla	130
Cadlinella ornatissima	120
Ceratosoma tenue	120
Chromodoris tinctoria	124
Chromodoris africana	120
Chromodoris annulata	120
Chromodoris boucheti	120
Chromodoris cf. geminus	122
Chromodoris conchyliata	120
Chromodoris fidelis	122
Chromodoris geminus	122
Chromodoris geometrica	122
Chromodoris hamiltoni	122
Chromodoris heatherae	122
Chromodoris tinctoria	124
Cuthona sp.	130
Dendrodoris denisoni	128
Doris sp.	118
Glossodoris atromarginata	124
Glossodoris cinta	124
Glossodoris pallida	124
Glossodoris sp.	124
Glossodoris symmetricus	124
Glossodoris undaurum	126
Gymnodoris rubropapulosa	116
Halgerda carlsoni	118
Halgerda dichromis	118
Halgerda tessellata	118
Halgerda toliara	118
Halgerda wasinensis	118
Hexabranchus sanguineus	116
Hydatina physis	116
Hydatina amplustre	116
Hypselodoris bullockii	126
Hypselodoros carnea	126
Hypselodoris fucata	126
Hypselodoris maculosa	126
Hypselodoris sp.	128
Hyselodoris rudmani	126
Janolus capensis	130
Micromelo undata	116
Nembrotha purpureolineata	116
Phyllidia ocellata	128
Phyllidia varicosa	128
Phyllidiella zeylanica	130
Phyllodesmium sp.	130
Pteraeolidia ianthina	130
Risbecia pulchella	128
Thorunna horologia	128